W9-CJN-472

DATE DUE

SEP 26 1989	JUN 10 1999		
OCT 16 1989	JUL 12 1999		
	NOV 9 1999	AUG 16 2011	
	APR 17 2002		
	NOV 04 2002	JAN 04 2013	
APR 05 1994		JAN 21 2014	
JUL 14 1994	DEC 23 2008		
NOV 28 1994	JAN 06 2008		DEC 15 2016
MAR 14 1995	APR 30 2008		MAY 31 2016
APR 17 1995			
MAY 18 1995	DEC 18 2010		
	APR 19 2011		
NOV 26 1998			
DEC 22 1998			
JAN 13 1999			
MAR 21 2002			

An Illustrated Treasury of

MYTHS AND LEGENDS

An Illustrated Treasury of

MYTHS AND LEGENDS

James Riordan
and Brenda Ralph Lewis

Illustrated by Victor Ambrus

Exeter Books

NEW YORK

Robin Hood Meets Little John was originally published in *Robin Hood: His Life and Legend* by Bernard Miles published in 1979. *King Arthur and the Round Table* was originally published in *Tales of King Arthur* by James Riordan published in 1982. Both were published by The Hamlyn Publishing Group Limited.

Contents

Theseus and the Minotaur

The best Greek legends were about their ancient heroes, men such as Theseus, or Perseus who killed the Gorgon, Jason who sought the Golden Fleece and Ulysses who won a victory over Troy. The Hellens, as the Greeks called themselves (it was the Romans who misnamed them Greeks) handed down their heroic deeds in song and story, embroidering on the way so that in the end, fact and fiction mingled inextricably. The Minotaur in this story literally means Minos Bull and probably originates in some Cretan religious ritual. Labyrinth comes from the Greek word for 'maze' and may well refer to the ancient and elaborate palace at Knossos in Crete, which was already in ruins when Greek civilisation began.

No full story of the early fortunes of Theseus has reached us. But the Greek writers Plutarch, born in about 46 BC, and Apollodorus, born about 180 BC, provide outlines of the legend.

Long ago, there lived in Athens a brave young king named Aegeus. He longed for a son to succeed him, so to help him decide who would give him a son, he went to Delphi to consult the oracle in the famous temple to Apollo. He was told to go to Trozen, across the sea from Athens, and there to woo and wed the king of Trozen's daughter, Aethra.

Aegeus did as he was advised and his wife soon became pregnant but even before their child was born he was anxious to return to Athens. He led his wife to a lonely grove of trees beside a mountain stream. 'Listen, wife, to what I say, for I must leave and shall not return. Soon our son will be born. You must call him Theseus. When he is eighteen years old, bring him to this grove and tell him to move this rock and take what is beneath it. You must then send him to me at Athens.' Within three days Aegeus was gone.

Making a mighty effort Theseus raised the rock and rolled it over with a triumphant shout. When he looked beneath it he saw a bronze sword with a glittering gold hilt, and by its side a pair of golden sandals.

As foretold, Aethra gave birth to a son and named him Theseus as his father had wished. He grew up brave and strong and gentle with his mother, yet with others he was often quick-tempered. No one was more daring in the hunt, nor more skilful in the use of sword and spear.

When he was eighteen his mother took him to the secret grove where she told him of his father's wishes and showed him the rock, telling him to move it if he could. Making a mighty effort Theseus raised the rock and rolled it over with a triumphant shout. When he looked beneath it he saw a bronze sword with a glittering gold hilt, and by its side a pair of golden sandals. Snatching them up he held them high above his head.

'Well done, my son,' his mother said, a tinge of sadness in her voice. 'Now you must journey to your father in Athens.' Then she kissed Theseus and wept, for she knew she would never see her son again.

Theseus set off northwards across a rocky plain towards the distant hills. His father's sword hung by his side and the golden sandals were upon his feet. He took the overland route to Athens although it held many perils. Bandits and monsters controlled the roads terrorizing those who passed. But Theseus bravely overcame all the dangers he encountered on his way to Athens. His fame travelled before him, and as, at last, he walked proudly into the city, all the people ran out to cheer him. 'Long live the hero Theseus.'

Boldly, he ascended the sacred steps into the Acropolis where his father's palace stood, and marched into the hall without a word. His heart beat wildly as he stood before his father, King Aegeus, but the king did not recognize him.

However, the sorceress Medea, Aegeus's new wife, easily identified the young man; she feared he would inherit his father's throne instead of her own son, Medus. She hissed in Aegeus's ear, 'This man has come to sieze your kingdom. Give him this poisoned cup of wine.'

Obediently, the old king took the cup and handed it to his son. Theseus was about to drink from it when, suddenly, his father spotted the sword hilt glittering at his thigh and the golden sandals on his feet. 'My son,' he cried, 'Stop, do not drink!'

As he spoke, he dashed the cup from the young man's hand, so that the wine spilled out, hissing, upon the floor. Instantly, Medea fled from the hall. She leapt into her winged chariot and was not seen again.

Aegeus looked at his son with misty eyes. The two men embraced each other and wept, until neither had any more tears to shed. Then Aegeus and Theseus stood on the balcony of the palace and Aegeus introduced his son to the people, shouting, 'Behold, my son. A better man than his father ever was. He will save our land from its suffering.'

So Theseus remained in Athens. He successfully led his father's army in battle and defeated Athens's enemies to his father's great pride and joy.

Yet when spring drew near, Aegeus and all the Athenians grew strangely sad and silent. Theseus could not understand it. Then a dreaded message arrived from King Minos of Crete. 'Send seven youths and seven girls as sacrifice to the Minotaur.'

Now the Minotaur was a terrible monster, with the body of a man and the head of a bull. It lived in a den in the middle of a high-walled labyrinth full of

The old king took the cup and handed it to his son. Theseus was about to drink from it when his father spotted the sword hilt glittering at his thigh and the golden sandals on his feet.

winding passages. The labyrinth was so built that once inside no one could ever find a way out. And the monster's only food was human flesh.

Since the labyrinth was in the city of Knossos within King Minos's island realm of Crete, it was King Minos's fate to keep the Minotaur fed with human flesh, so that it did not come out to eat the Cretans. Every year, seven young men and seven young women were chosen from cities that gave allegiance to King Minos, to feed the beast. Athens paid its due every ninth year, and its turn had come round again.

As soon as he heard of this appalling sacrifice, Theseus told his father, 'I shall go myself with the young people and kill the Minotaur.'

Despite Aegeus's pleas, his mind was made up, and his father had to let him go. 'But promise me this,' Aegeus said. 'If you return, though that is unlikely, take down the black sail of your ship and hoist a white one instead. I shall be watching from the cliffs and will know from afar that you are safe.'

Theseus promised, and with the thirteen other young people, set off in the black-sailed ship of sorrow. The families left on the shore were distraught with grief, but Theseus tried to cheer up his companions. 'Have hope, my friends,' he said, 'for I have slain many monsters in the past.'

At last they came to Crete, and to Knossos, beneath the peaks of Ida, and to the palace of King Minos. Theseus and his companions stood before the king who immediately imprisoned them all, to be cast to the monster one by one.

But Ariadne, Minos's daughter, catching sight of the handsome prince, fell instantly in love with him. She was determined to save Theseus if she could.

So, that night she went down to the dungeons and told him of a plan she had made. 'My lord, I will give you a special sword with which to slay the beast, and a ball of thread to unwind as you go into the labyrinth, so you can find your way out by it. Only promise me that if you escape you will take me back with you to Athens, for my father will surely kill me if he knows what I have done.

Theseus thanked her, and gave her his word, then lay down to rest.

When evening came, the guards led Theseus out first to meet the Minotaur. Upon entering the labyrinth, the brave young man followed winding paths among the rocks, passed under caverns and arches and galleries, climbed over piles of bones and fallen stone. He turned left and right, went up and down till his head swam. But all the time he held fast to his thread, for when he had entered the maze he had tied it to a stone and let it unroll as he went on. Just when the thread was almost finished he heard a muffled roar, a snuffling and a trampling of feet. He was getting nearer and nearer to the Minotaur.

As he rounded a bend, he saw it—a strange and grotesque beast. Its body, though dark and shaggy, was clearly like that of some huge man, but its massive sharp-horned head was like that of a wild bull. Bellowing loudly, the monster lowered its head and charged full tilt at Theseus. Nimbly, the young man stepped aside and, as the monster passed, aimed a sword thrust at its neck.

The Minotaur howled with pain and rage—never before had it felt a wound. It turned and charged again with a mighty roar. Again and again. And so the fight went on until at last the Minotaur had received so many wounds its strength began to fail. With one last mighty effort, Theseus drove his sword straight through the monster's throat and it rolled over, dead.

Then the hero felt his way back along the thread until he came to the mouth of that terrible maze. Ariadne was overjoyed as she saw him stagger out.

'It is done,' he gasped, showing her the blood-stained sword.

Swiftly they went back to the dungeons, opened all the doors and set the prisoners free. The Athenians with Ariadne fled to their ship, leapt on board and hoisted up the sail. And as the night was dark and starless, no one saw them escape into the open sea.

Meanwhile, old Aegeus sat on the cliffs near Athens, day after day, straining his eyes across the sea, hoping to see a white sail gleam.

Alas, so eager was Theseus to reach home that he had forgotten to hoist up the white sail. And so, when his father spied the black sail on the sea, he thought his son was dead. In his great grief, he threw himself into the sea, which is called the Aegean to this day.

By sad fate, therefore, Theseus became king of Athens and ruled wisely and well for many years. Athenians still honour him as their law giver and the father of their freedom.

As Theseus rounded a bend, he saw it—a strange and grotesque beast. Its body, though dark and shaggy, was clearly like that of some huge man, but its massive sharp-horned head was like that of a wild bull.

Perseus and Medusa

Perseus, one of the greatest heroes of Greek mythology, led a very adventurous life. Half-human, and half-god, he rescued his future wife Andromeda from a rock where she had been chained as a sacrifice to a huge sea serpent. Perseus also turned Atlas, King of Mauretania, into a great mountain, Mount Atlas. Afterwards, the Greeks believed, Atlas had to carry the Earth and Heavens on his shoulders. Against Atlas, Perseus used the head of the Gorgon Medusa whose eyes were so terrible to look at that all who did so were at once turned to stone. The way Perseus obtained Medusa's head provided his most thrilling adventure–but he could not have done it without the help of his father Zeus and the other Greek gods.

In Ancient Greece one day long ago, a large chest was thrown up onto the beach on the tiny island of Seraphos. Dictys, the fisherman who found it, was startled to discover that inside the chest, all wet and bedraggled, there was a beautiful girl and her baby son. The girl, Danae, had an amazing story to tell.

She was a princess, the daughter of King Acrisius of Argos, and her misfortunes had begun when her father was given terrible news by the Oracle at Delphi. 'You will one day have a grandson who will kill you,' the Oracle had said.

Danae was the King's only child, and he resolved that she would never marry, and have children of her own. That way, the King thought, he could never have a grandson, and so the Oracle's prediction could never come true.

So, Acrisius had imprisoned Danae in an underground house made of bronze, and he intended she should remain there until she died. Acrisius, however, reckoned without the gods on Mount Olympus. Zeus, the father of the gods, saw the beautiful Danae as she sat alone and sad in her bronze house, and he fell in love with her. Zeus turned himself into a shower of gold and entered the house through an opening in the roof.

Afterwards, Danae found she was expecting a child, and when her son, Perseus, was born, she tried to conceal him from her father Acrisius. But Acrisius found out, so he set Danae and his grandson adrift on the sea in a large chest.

All night, the chest tossed about on the waves and Danae began to fear that she and Perseus would drown. But Zeus was watching over them, and at dawn next day, the god made a great wave carry the chest ashore on Seraphos.

So, the young mother and her child were saved.

The fisherman Dictys was a kind-hearted soul and he was deeply affected by Danae's sad tale. He took Danae and her baby home to his wife and there, in a humble fisherman's cottage by the sea, Perseus grew up to be a strong and handsome young man.

The ruler of Seraphos was King Polydectes. He was a cruel and unpleasant man, but when he saw Danae, he was very much attracted by her beauty, and married her. The trouble was, though, that Polydectes hated young Perseus. The King had a jealous nature and could not bear the thought of a rival for the love of Danae, who adored her son.

Polydectes decided he must get rid of Perseus. So, he encouraged the young man to leave Seraphos and go on a great adventure: to find the terrifying Gorgon, Medusa, and cut off her head. If Perseus could accomplish that, Polydectes assured him, he would become a great and famous hero.

Perseus, being young and trusting, thought the idea was very exciting. He did not realise that Polydectes, like his grandfather Acrisius before him, was planning to send him to his death.

Medusa was a horrible creature, one of three sisters, the Gorgons, who lived together on an island. The Gorgons were ghastly to look at. They were winged monsters with hands made of brass, tusks instead of teeth, and in place of hair, their heads were covered in a mass of hissing, writhing snakes. Two of the Gorgons were immortal, but the third, Medusa, was mortal and could therefore

The ruler of Seraphos was King Polydectes. He was a cruel and unpleasant man, but when he saw Danae he was very much attracted by her beauty.

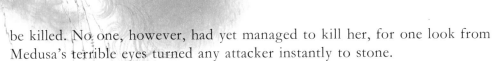

be killed. No one, however, had yet managed to kill her, for one look from Medusa's terrible eyes turned any attacker instantly to stone.

The Greek gods were worried to see Perseus setting off to meet this monstrous creature without knowing the terrible danger he faced. So, they resolved to help him.

First, they sent Hermes the messenger of the gods, to Perseus. Perseus knew at once who Hermes was because the god wore sandals and a cap with wings attached, and carried a wand decorated with a pair of serpents.

'You can never succeed against Medusa unless you have four things,' Hermes told Perseus. 'The first is a pair of winged sandals. The second is a magic wallet and the third, Pluto's helmet of invisibility. The last is a sword which is strong and has the sharpest blade of any in the whole world.'

Hermes gave Perseus the sword he needed. It had a magnificent curved blade. For the rest, Hermes told Perseus, he must find the Nymphs of the North who had the winged sandals, the helmet and the wallet in their possession.

Finding the Nymphs would not be easy, for only the Grey Women knew where they lived and they could be difficult to persuade. But Hermes knew a way to get the information out of them and he told Perseus how it could be done.

Just then, a sudden bright glow appeared in the sky. Perseus gazed at it in amazement. It was the goddess Athena, surrounded by brilliant light, descending to Earth.

Athena carried a shining shield, which she gave to Perseus. 'My shield will be your mirror, Perseus,' said Athena. 'Remember you must not look directly at Medusa, or you will be turned at once to stone: instead, you must look at her reflection in my shield. That way, you can approach her safely.'

When Athena had gone, Hermes and Perseus set off for the end of the Earth where the Grey Women lived. The Women were strange, ugly creatures. They had only one eye and one tooth between them, and took turns to look through the eye and eat with the tooth.

When Hermes and Perseus reached the place where the Grey Women lived, Perseus did as the god had told him. He crept up behind the Women and snatched away their eye and their tooth. The Women, all of them now blind and faced with starvation, howled in rage and fear. But Perseus refused to give back the eye and tooth until they had told him the way to the Nymphs of the North. The Women screamed and cried and protested, but in the end, they gave in and told Perseus.

When Perseus arrived at the Nymphs' island, they were only too pleased to help him. They gave him the winged sandals and helmet and the magic wallet which could change size depending on what it had to carry.

Perseus refused to give back the eye and tooth until they had told him the way to the Nymphs of the North.

Perseus snatched up
Medusa's severed head,
and the snakes that
covered it hissed and
writhed.

At last, Perseus possessed everything he required to attack Medusa successfully, and he sped through the air in the winged sandals, over land, and sea, until the island of the Gorgons came in sight. As Perseus looked down from the sky, he could see what appeared to be statues standing in the fields. But they were not statues at all. They were the forms of men and animals who had been turned to stone.

Then, far below, Perseus noticed the scaly shapes of the Gorgons themselves lying asleep in the sun with their wings folded.

'Which one is Medusa?' he wondered. 'They all look the same!'

'The one nearest the shore is Medusa,' a voice said. It was Athena, who was watching over Perseus as he faced his perilous task.

Perseus moved Athena's bright shield to and fro until he saw Medusa's reflection in it. Then, concentrating on the image in the shield, he flew down towards the island, gathering speed as he went. As soon as he was close enough, Perseus raised the great curved sword which Hermes had given him, and swung it towards Medusa's neck.

The sword sliced right through. Perseus snatched up Medusa's severed head, and as the snakes that covered it hissed and writhed, he pushed it into the magic wallet and quickly fastened it.

Below him, Medusa's headless body thrashed about, its metal scales clashing against the rocks. Perseus wasted no time. He sprang high up into the air, just avoiding the great claws of Medusa's sisters who had been woken by the noise. Perseus' winged sandals took him speeding away towards the horizon, and although Medusa's sisters flew after him, roaring with rage, they were unable to catch him, for the magic helmet made him invisible. So he escaped, leaving the island of the terrible Gorgons far behind him.

The Revenge of Isis

The goddess Isis, wife of the god Osiris, was one of the most powerful and skilful of Ancient Egyptian deities. It was Isis who introduced agriculture into Egypt and who taught people how to cure diseases with medicines and restore the sick to health.

Isis is best known, though, for the part she played in avenging the murder of her husband, and for the way she protected her son Horus so that he could survive the plots against him and take his rightful place as King-Pharoah of Egypt. The story is a sad one, for like the story of Siegfried, it is a family tragedy. The villain is Isis' own brother, Set.

Isis was a great queen, able to govern Egypt wisely while her husband was absent. The people of Egypt were grateful to her for all the skills she had taught them, and both loved and respected her.

However, not everyone felt this way about Isis. Her young brother, Set, hated and envied her and her husband Osiris, and was always scheming to overthrow them. Set, of course, wanted their powers for himself.

One day, soon after Osiris returned to Egypt from travels abroad, Set invited him to a banquet. The banquet was magnificent and everyone enjoyed themselves and felt relaxed and happy that Osiris was home again. Set was in a very jolly mood and was extremely gracious towards his chief guest, Osiris. Osiris began to think that Set was not, after all, the dangerous enemy he and Isis had previously supposed.

After the feast was over, Set called on his guests to play a game. There was a splendid chest in the banqueting hall, so beautiful and costly that anyone would be glad to own it.

'I will give this chest to anyone who can lie down flat in it,' Set offered.

Several of the guests jumped up, anxious to make the attempt, but none of them succeeded. Some were too fat. Others were too tall.

Then, Set asked Osiris to lie down in the chest. Osiris, laughing, agreed. What he did not know, however, was that the villainous Set had had the chest made especially to fit him–and no one else. As soon as Osiris climbed into the chest and lay down, Set and his henchmen rushed over, slammed the lid shut and hammered nails in to secure it. Then, before anyone could stop them, the conspirators tied lead weights to the chest and flung it into the River Nile. Although the chest was very heavy it did not sink. The strong river current moved it along towards the sea where, Set hoped, it would be lost for ever and Osiris with it. Set now made himself King-Pharoah of Egypt in Osiris' place.

When Isis heard how her husband had been murdered by her brother, she wept bitterly. Grief-stricken, she changed her fine clothes for the dull, plain robes which widows wore, and as a sign of mourning, cut off half her hair.

Now, Isis began searching for the body of her husband. She wandered through Egypt, asking everyone she met if they had seen the chest. At last, some children told her they had seen it drifting along the Nile towards the sea. Following this clue and guided by the gods, Isis discovered that the sea tides had carried the chest over to the coast of Phoenicia, where it had drifted ashore to rest on the sand beneath a tamarisk tree.

The chest, however, would not be easy to find, for the tamarisk had grown all round it hiding it from sight. King Malacander of Byblos in Phoenicia had seen and admired the huge tamarisk and decided he must have it in his palace. So, the tree had been cut down and taken to the palace, where Malacander had it set up as a pillar, and the chest had gone with it.

Isis was determined to retrieve her husband's body, so she travelled to Byblos and entered Malacander's palace without telling anyone who she was. There, Isis made friends with the maids who attended Queen Astarte, Malacander's wife and the mother of a newborn son.

When she next saw her maids, Queen Astarte noticed there was something strange about them. There was a heavenly perfume about Isis and she had

As soon as Osiris climbed into the chest and lay down, Set and his henchmen rushed over, slammed the lid shut and hammered nails in to secure it.

given some of it to her new friends. When they told the Queen about the mysterious newcomer to the palace, she at once ordered that Isis be brought to her, that she might judge her for herself.

Astarte asked Isis to become nurse to her baby son and Isis agreed. Isis, who had no children of her own, grew to love the little boy and decided to use her magic powers to make him immortal, so that he would live for ever. The task of transforming a human being into an immortal took a long time, and one day, before Isis had completed the process, Queen Astarte made a surprise visit to her son and his nurse. Unfortunately, just at that moment, Isis had used her magic to turn herself into a swallow. Astarte was greatly alarmed to see her flying round the huge tamarisk tree in which the body of Osiris was imprisoned. Astarte screamed with shock, and as soon as she did so, the spell Isis had cast over the baby was broken. So, the little boy lost all chance of becoming immortal.

Because of Astarte's discovery, Isis was now forced to reveal who she was, and why she had come to Malacander's palace.

At that moment, Isis had used her magic to turn herself into a swallow. Astarte was greatly alarmed to see her flying round the huge tamarisk tree.

Malacander felt extremely sorry for Isis and gave her the tamarisk tree. Quickly, Isis cut away the tree and at last found the chest which contained the body of Osiris. Flinging herself across it, Isis wept and wailed with renewed grief. The sounds of her grieving were so terrible that the newborn baby could not bear them and quite suddenly, the little boy died.

Now it was the turn of the King and Queen to weep and mourn their tragic loss. Even so, they felt no anger against Isis, and the King gave her a ship so that she could take the dead Osiris back across the sea to Egypt. As a further sign of his sympathy for her, Malacander sent his elder son with Isis as a companion. But this boy, too, was fated to die.

Once on board the ship, Isis opened the chest and on seeing Osiris lying in it, began again to weep with heartbreak and sorrow.

'If only I had given Osiris a son to become King in Egypt and punish Set for his terrible crime!' Isis cried in despair. 'But I have no son and now Osiris is dead, I can never have his child.'

Malacander's son came up to her, hoping to comfort her, but Isis turned on him with such a fearful look on her face that the boy leapt back in fright. He lost his footing on the deck and before he could save himself, fell overboard into the sea and was drowned.

Now, Isis was alone in her misery. But then, she discovered that a miracle had occurred. Before the ship reached Egypt, she found that she was expecting a child. Isis realised that she would be in great danger if Set ever learned about her child or knew that she had managed to retrieve the body of Osiris. So, when the ship reached Egypt, Isis hid in the marshes near the mouth of the Nile and there awaited the birth of the son who would take revenge for Osiris' murder.

Isis' plan, however, went wrong. Quite by chance, Set arrived in the marshlands for some hunting. One moonlit night, he discovered the chest and looking into it recognised Osiris, whom he had never thought to see again. Frightened and furious, Set seized the body and ripped it into fourteen parts. Then, Set ordered that the parts should be scattered all over Egypt so that Osiris would never be a threat to him again.

Once again, though, Set failed to realise how strong and determined Isis was. She began travelling all over Egypt, seeking the pieces of her husband's body. Each time she found one, she erected a stele, a pillar which served as a gravestone.

'Set will think that Osiris' body has been buried in different places,' Isis told herself. 'So he will never know my purpose.'

Isis' purpose was to remake the body of Osiris and at last, after a very long time and much searching, she was able to do so. Then, Isis spread precious oils over Osiris, embalming and preserving his body so that he was once again an immortal being.

Unfortunately, Set discovered that Isis had returned to Egypt and ordered her to be seized and thrown into prison. Isis was now in great peril, for Set might find out about the child she was expecting.

'I must get out of this place,' she decided. 'Or Set will kill me, and my child, the son of Osiris, will die with me.'

Isis turned for help to Thoth, who had once been Osiris' vizier, or chief minister. Thoth helped Isis to escape from prison, and she fled back to the Nile marshlands where seven serpents watched over her until the time came for her child to be born.

At last, Isis gave birth to a son, Horus, and for the first time in many years, she felt great joy and happiness.

'When my son grows up he will avenge his father and overthrow my evil brother Set,' Isis resolved. Yet she knew that she would need all her magic to preserve Horus from Set, who, when he learned of the child's birth, would undoubtedly try to find him and kill him.

Set did, indeed, attempt to kill Horus, by turning himself into a poisonous snake and biting the little boy as he lay hidden among the reeds in the marshes. Once more, though, Osiris' vizier, Thoth, came to the rescue and called on Ra, the Sun, and the greatest of the gods, to save the child. In Ra's name, Thoth cast a powerful spell on Horus and the boy was cured.

Horus was never again to face such peril, for having so nearly lost her precious son, Isis redoubled her efforts to protect him with all the magic and all the healing arts at her command.

In time, her loving care was well rewarded. Horus grew to be a great warrior and when, finally, he challenged his evil uncle Set, he won a great victory. There was a mighty battle in which Set was vanquished and killed. So, Osiris was avenged and Horus took his rightful place as King-Pharoah of Egypt.

When Set discovered that Isis had returned to Egypt, he ordered her to be seized and thrown into prison.

27

Romulus and Remus

The Romans had no true mythology of their own, but when they conquered Greece, they took over the Greek legends and gods and worshipped them under Roman names. It is mainly the Romans we have to thank for much of Greek mythology which might otherwise have been lost. However, the story of the founding of Rome is one of the few purely Roman stories.

Romulus is regarded as one of the two ancestors of the Romans (the other is Aeneas) and all Roman documents date from 753 BC, the year in which he was supposed to have founded the city.

Romulus and Remus were twins. Many people believed they were the sons of Mars, the god of war, for their mother, Silvia, had been shut up in the temple of Mars by her wicked uncle, Amulius. He had seized the throne in Latinum from his brother, Numitor, murdered his nephews, and thus hoped to prevent Silvia from having sons who could rightfully claim the throne.

His evil plan, however, did not succeed, for Romulus and Remus were born. As soon as he heard the news of the birth of his great-nephews, Amulius was determined to kill them, and he summoned two trusty servants. 'Take the babies from the temple,' he ordered them, 'and drown them in the River Tiber.'

So in the dead of night, the two men stole into the temple while Silvia was asleep, and carried off the babies in their cradle. They took the cradle to the river to complete the evil deed, and they dropped it into the fast-flowing waters.

'The babies are dead,' they told the king.

The cradle, however, floated like a tiny boat downstream, bobbing and dipping in the waves, but it did not sink or overturn. The two boys slept on,

In the dead of night, the two men stole into the temple and carried off the babies in their cradle. They took the cradle to the river to complete the evil deed, and dropped it into the fast-flowing waters.

lulled by the murmuring of the waves and the rocking of their cradle. As dawn broke, it came to rest in a clump of rushes at the foot of the Palatine Hill. It was not long before the twins were hungry, cold and scared.

Their crying echoed across the grassy hills and was heard by a she-wolf as she came to drink from the river. Curious at the unfamiliar sounds, she followed the cries to their source and looked inside the cradle. Bewildered by the sight of two human babies, she stood there, head leaning to one side, uncertain what to do. Finally, her motherly instincts overcame her fear of man, and one by one she gently picked up the infants in her mouth, and took them ashore. She carried them to her hillside cave, and began to bring them up as wolf cubs.

As the months passed by, the little boys grew up strong and healthy and sometimes toddled off, but always beneath the watchful eye of their foster-mother wolf. One day a shepherd, Faustulus, passed nearby and heard their strange grunts. He stealthily made his way up the hill, then stopped in his tracks, unable to believe his eyes. In front of a cave, children were playing happily with wolf cubs. Faustulus quickly picked up the boys and ran off home before the wolf could pounce.

The shepherd and his wife had no children of their own, so they were overjoyed to rear the two wolf-boys. It was not long before the twins forgot their animal life and grew up as shepherd lads, helping their new parents guard the royal flocks. They became strong and handsome youths, yet never quite threw off all their wild ways. Now and again, they would ambush bandits on the lonely mountain roads, sharing out the spoils with poor local shepherds.

Soon their fame as champions of the poor spread to the ears of their grandfather Numitor, who was living out a lonely life in a hillside barn. Asking his guards to bring the young men to him, he was at once struck by their likeness to his daughter, Silvia, and wondered if by some miracle his two grandsons could still be alive. When he learned their story, he realized the truth and told the boys the rest of the tale.

'You are, in truth, the sons of my poor imprisoned daughter, my royal grandsons. Your wicked uncle Amulius tried to kill you and steal your birthright. You must one day right the wrong.'

Romulus and Remus were as cunning as they were wild, and they planned revenge on the wicked king. Gaining the support of shepherds and poor people they had helped, they gathered together a band of men. One night they attacked the palace and killed the king. Numitor was soon restored to the throne and Silvia was released from the temple. When all that was done Romulus and Remus thought of a great plan. They would build a city to mark the spot where they were found. It would be right at the foot of the Palatine Hill, beside the River Tiber surrounded by the seven hills. The city would be the grandest in the world.

Romulus designed plans for streets and houses; Remus for baths and temples. And a magnificent city grew up on the river banks.

But, alas, when it was built, the two brothers fell out. They quarrelled over its name.

'It shall be Reme, after me,' claimed Remus. 'I designed the temples of the

gods and the city shall be famous for its magnificent buildings.'

'No, it shall be Rome, after me,' said Romulus. 'It was I who planned the people's homes.'

And they came to blows—just as their grandfather and his brother had done. The wolf's milk in their blood made them savage foes. No fight between two men was ever so cruel and bloody; and it could not cease until one lay dead. Romulus won the fight and cast the body of his brother into the foundations for the city's gates.

So the city was called Rome.

Unforgiving though he was in battle, Romulus was a just and clever king. He created temples to the gods, the grandest being to Jupiter and Mars. He made laws and set up a council of city fathers, or patricians, as they were known, to ensure his laws were kept. He even built a shelter on the Palatine slopes for slaves who ran away.

So well and justly did he rule that the gods looked favourably upon him. One day, when he was already old and in council with his men, thunder was suddenly heard, and lightning forked across the sky, and then all went dark. As the darkness melted into light, the council saw that Romulus was gone.

He had been taken up to Mount Olympus to live among the gods and they made him Quirinus, a god of war. From then on, Romans worshipped him along with Jupiter and Mars. And Rome, the city he had founded, became in time the greatest in the world.

No fight between two men was ever so cruel and bloody; it could not cease until one lay dead. Romulus won the fight and cast the body of his brother into the foundations for the city's gates.

31

Gilgamesh the Mighty Warrior

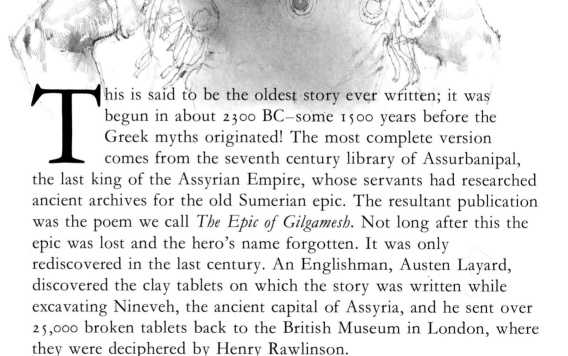

This is said to be the oldest story ever written; it was begun in about 2300 BC–some 1500 years before the Greek myths originated! The most complete version comes from the seventh century library of Assurbanipal, the last king of the Assyrian Empire, whose servants had researched ancient archives for the old Sumerian epic. The resultant publication was the poem we call *The Epic of Gilgamesh*. Not long after this the epic was lost and the hero's name forgotten. It was only rediscovered in the last century. An Englishman, Austen Layard, discovered the clay tablets on which the story was written while excavating Nineveh, the ancient capital of Assyria, and he sent over 25,000 broken tablets back to the British Museum in London, where they were deciphered by Henry Rawlinson.

The Sumerians were the first literate inhabitants of Mesopotamia (between the rivers Euphrates and Tigris, roughly in present-day Iraq) and theirs is the language of the oldest tablets which relate to Gilgamesh. Scholars have established that a king named Gilgamesh did live in southern Babylonia about 2700 BC.

Whurary hen the gods made Gilgamesh, they created a perfectly formed man. Shamash the sun god granted him beauty, and Adad the storm god gave him courage. He was two thirds god and one third man.

Yet when he was young he used his power savagely and became a tyrant king. The citizens of Uruk, his capital, were terrified of him and the gods took pity on them. They decided to send down to earth another man, Gilgamesh's equal in power and beauty. The goddess of creation, Aruru, fashioned a clay figure which she let fall into the wilderness, and thus Enkidu, the wild man of nature, was created.

He had a rough hairy body and long hair that waved in the wind. The goddess Anu shared her own clothing with him, and then, holding his hand, she led him like a child into a shepherd's tent.

All the shepherds crowded round and gave him bread and wine. But Enkidu would only suck the milk of wild beasts; it took time for him to learn how to eat bread and drink wine.

For several weeks he lived with the shepherds, and was their guardian, hunting wolves and lions so that the herdsmen could sleep in peace. One day, the shepherds told him about Gilgamesh's tyranny. 'I will go to Uruk,' he said, white with rage. 'I will challenge him and try to set things right.'

So Enkidu travelled to Uruk, and as he entered the town, people stood back in awe for he was the image of Gilgamesh.

'Now Gilgamesh has met his match,' they said.

Enkidu searched out Gilgamesh and confronted him. Soon they were wrestling like two wild bulls, knocking down doorposts, tents and market stalls. The walls of houses and even the earth itself shook. Finally, Gilgamesh managed to trip his opponent and instantly his fury cooled. 'Stranger,' he said. 'You are as strong as an ox and as noble as a king. Let us be friends. Come and live with me and teach me your ways.'

So Enkidu and Gilgamesh embraced and their friendship was sealed, and Gilgamesh no longer terrorised his subjects.

Some time passed and Gilgamesh became more and more restless for adventure. 'Let us go to the cedar forest and kill the demon giant Humbaba,' he suggested to his friend. 'Then the gods will be very pleased with us.'

Enkidu sighed. He knew by this time how reckless his friend could be. 'Humbaba is guardian of the great cedar forest. When he roars it is like a torrent in a storm; his breath is like fire; his jaws are death itself. When a deer moves a vast distance away, Humbaba hears it. He would kill us as soon as we set foot in the forest.'

But the headstrong Gilgamesh would not be put off. 'I shall ask the sun god for protection.'

So Gilgamesh chose two goats, one brown and one pure white, and took them to the sun god. 'Grant me your protection, O Shamash,' he said. 'I offer these kids as gifts.'

Shamash saw Gilgamesh was determined on his actions so he accepted the goats and granted Gilgamesh strong allies: the north wind, the whirlwind, the searing and icy winds, the tempest and the squall.

33

Anu created a heavenly bull which killed five hundred of Gilgamesh's warriors before it was finally killed by the king and Enkidu.

Gilgamesh and Enkidu set off. In three days, they had walked as much as a normal person could walk in a month. They crossed seven mountains before they reached the gate of the cedar forest. Then together they went down a grassy slope and came to a halt, struck dumb by the incredible height of the cedar trees. But Gilgamesh was still not afraid, and with a grin to his friend, defiantly began to fell a giant tree.

Far off, giant Humbaba heard the noise and flew into a violent rage. 'Who is trespassing in my woods and cutting down my trees?' he roared. He strode through the forest until he came upon the two intruders. Towering above them, he shook his shaggy beard and fixed a deathly eye upon brave Gilgamesh. The king's courage almost failed, but at that moment glorious Shamash, the sun god, came to his aid, summoning the winds. They came like dragons, like scorching fire, like flood and forked lightning. They buffeted Humbaba, beat against him, so that he was powerless to move.

Gilgamesh seized his chance. Drawing his sword, with Enkidu at his side, he struck at the giant. One thrust pierced his foot and, as he stumbled another went through his neck. At the third stroke, Humbaba, guardian of the forest, died.

The mountains and all the hills rejoiced at their freedom, but the giant's terrible cedars trembled with rage when their master fell. Swiftly, the two companions went into action. They felled the trees and cleared their roots as far as the banks of the river Euphrates. There they embraced, and flung Humbaba's severed head into the waters.

Gilgamesh washed his long hair in the river and cleaned his weapons; tossing back his hair to dry in the sun, he stood proudly on the bank. Ishtar, goddess of love and queen of heaven, saw how handsome the young king was and wished to have him for herself. 'Come to me, Gilgamesh,' she called down softly. 'I will harness a chariot of gold and lapis lazuli for you, with golden wheels and decorations of bronze. Kings and queens from mountain and plain will bow before you and bring you gifts.'

But Enkidu warned his friend; 'Don't listen to her. She is cruel to men and beasts. She loved the strong lion; now she digs traps for him. She loved the wild stallion; now she makes whips and spurs to torment him. She loved the shepherd, then turned him into a wolf whom his own dogs chase away. She loved the minder of the palm grove, then changed him to a blind mole to live deep in the ground. If you wed her, you too will suffer a similar fate.'

Gilgamesh, for once, listened to his friend's advice, and told Ishtar, 'I will not take you as my wife.'

When Ishtar heard this she flew into a rage and called on Anu, the father of all the gods to help her revenge herself on Gilgamesh for insulting her. Anu created a heavenly bull which killed five hundred of Gilgamesh's warriors before it was itself finally killed by the king and Enkidu. The two friends then poured oil into the horns of the bull and offered them to Shamash.

Everywhere, Gilgamesh was hailed as the mightiest warrior of all men. The two friends were proud and happy but their rejoicing was shortlived. Enkidu was taken ill, and it was soon evident to everyone that the king's close friend was dying. Gilgamesh cared for his friend himself and nursed him lovingly, but

'Let me see the light of the Sun until my eyes are dazzled with looking', begged Gilgamesh. 'Now that I have come so far, am I one day to die and let the earth cover my head for ever?'

one dark night, when Gilgamesh, exhausted, had fallen asleep on a chair beside the bed, Enkidu died.

When Gilgamesh awoke, he realized instantly that his friend's spirit had left his body, and in an agony of grief, threw himself upon the bed, tearing his hair, ripping his royal robes and roaring his love and anguish. For seven days and nights he wept for Enkidu then, so that his memory should not fade, he had a splendid statue built.

The death of his friend had unnerved Gilgamesh. He was afraid of death and he wanted to find eternal life. He resolved to go to the far-off land of Dilmun, to the garden of the gods. There he would contact Utnapishtim; the only man to whom the gods had granted everlasting life.

Gilgamesh set off on his journey, and at last came to Mashu, the great twin peaks that guarded the rising and setting of the Sun. He followed the Sun's road through the mountains, to its rising, until he was enclosed by darkness. He could see nothing ahead, nor behind. For twelve leagues the blackness hemmed him in, until suddenly the sunlight streamed down. He had come to the garden of the gods, by the edge of the sea.

The bushes around him were covered in glittering gems. There was fruit made of cornelian, with lapis lazuli leaves. Thorns and thistles were made of agate and pearl from the sea.

As Gilgamesh was walking in this earthly paradise, he heard a voice challenging him. It was Utnapishtim.

'No mortal man can come this way,' said the guardian. 'Nor will he as long

36

as the winds drive over the sea, for the waters of death close the entrance.'

'Let me see the lights of the Sun until my eyes are dazzled with looking,' begged Gilgamesh. 'Now that I have come so far, am I one day to die and let the earth cover my head forever? Surely that cannot be so? Give me everlasting life.'

'No, Gilgamesh,' said Utnapishtim. 'You will never find the life you seek. When the gods created humankind they created death, not everlasting life. You, like all men, should fill your belly with good food. Dance and be merry day and night; feast and rejoice. Wear fresh clothes, wash in cool water, cherish the little child that holds your hand. And make your wife happy. For that, too, is the fate of men.'

'But how is it that you came to enter the company of the gods?' asked Gilgamesh, dismayed at failing in his quest.

'When the great flood came,' said Utnapishtim, 'My wife and I were in my reed boat upon a river. For six days and nights winds blew, tempest and torrent overwhelmed the world. On the seventh day the storm grew still, the sea calm and the flood receded. As I looked at the face of the world there was silence, and all humankind was turned to clay.

'Then Enlil, god of earth and air, came to our boat, took us by the hand and led us out. Touching our foreheads, he said: "In time past Utnapishtim was a mortal man; but henceforth he and his wife will live forever as the guardians of my river mouths."'

Then Gilgamesh accepted his fate and leaving the garden of the gods, he went back the way he had come, arriving in due course at Uruk. He spent his remaining days adding to the glory of his city so that one third was gardens, one third fields and one third homes. But he left space for a temple that was to be his tomb and eventually he lay there at peace.

Idun's Golden Apples

Norsemen saw the universe in three layers. At the top was Asgard, the home of the gods. Also on the top floor was Valhalla, the vast hall of dead warriors who were looked after by Valkyries, maidservants of the gods.

Across a rainbow bridge was the middle layer called Midgard, inhabited by humans and surrounded by a huge ocean. Jotunheim, the land of giants, lay at the edge of Midgard.

At the bottom, was the land of the dead, Niflheim, presided over by an ogress called Hel.

The story of Idun is one of the best known Norse legends and shows clearly the evil and mercurial character of Loki. Like most myths of the Norsemen, Idun's story was only written down long after the gods and goddesses had passed into legend, usually by Christian priests in the thirteenth century.

Odin, chief of the gods, had many sons. One, called Bragi, grew up to be very handsome, a fine word-smith and god of poetry.

As Bragi walked in Midgard, one day, he met Idun. The daughter of a dwarf, she was fair, lovely and kind. They fell in love and, together they went to Asgard, home of the gods. There, Idun was made guardian of the golden apples, which the gods ate to stay eternally young.

Once, the gods Odin, Hoenir and Loki, the fire-god, crossed the rainbow Bifrost into Midgard and travelled through the world, when they came to a lonely valley in the hills. Hungry and tired, they killed an ox and set it to roast on a blazing fire. When they thought the ox was cooked, they eagerly began to carve it. Yet, to their surprise, the meat was still raw. Again they waited, banking up the fire, but strangely the ox would not cook. The sun had all but crossed the sky, a chill wind blew down the valley and the three gods shivered.

'There is evil here,' said Odin.

Once more they piled wood upon the fire, thrust the ox meat on to it, and waited patiently. But the meat did not even singe.

All of a sudden, they heard a deep-throated cackle. They looked up and there, in an oak tree, sat an eagle, staring at them with cruel, black eyes. 'If you share your meal with me,' it said, 'your ox will cook.'

'Welcome, friend,' replied Odin. 'Eat your fill then, but let our ox roast, for we are starving.'

With a screech and flapping of its wings, the bird swooped low, fanning the flames. In no time, the meat was sizzling and ready to be eaten.

'I cooked the meat. Mine is first bite,' the eagle croaked, picking up the rump and shoulders in its claws.

Angry at the eagle's greed, Loki thrust his staff at the bird, making it drop the meat. With a screech of fury, the eagle rose into the air, clutching the staff. To his alarm, Loki found he was caught fast to one end of it, and he was carried, kicking and yelling, into the sky. The eagle soared but then swooped low over sharp rocks and thorny thickets, so that poor Loki was bumped and bruised. 'Help! Mercy! Who are you?' he cried.

'I am Thiazi the storm giant,' replied the bird, 'disguised in my eagle-cloak which I use to bring storms.'

'What do you want with me?' cried Loki, as his back was skinned on an icy slope and his arms were almost wrenched from their sockets.

'Idun and her apples of everlasting youth,' the eagle said. 'Bring them to the valley in seven days.'

Anxious to be free, Loki promised to bring Idun to the storm giant. Next moment, Loki was falling to the rocky ground where he landed painfully. Limping back to his two companions, he said nothing of his promise. He could not break his word, so somehow he had to steal Idun from her husband Bragi.

Six days passed, then Loki thought of a plan. When Bragi was away, he went to find Idun. 'Idun,' said Loki, 'what do you think? Deep in a forest across the rainbow Bifrost, I found a tree bearing golden apples just like yours.'

'That cannot be,' said Idun, frowning. 'Only I have apples that give the gods eternal youth.'

With a screech of fury, the eagle rose into the air, clutching the staff. To his alarm, Loki found he was caught fast to one end of it, and he was carried, kicking and yelling, into the sky.

40

'That's strange,' mused Loki slyly. 'I saw them with my own eyes. Perhaps we should go together and gather them for the gods?'

'Lead me to the tree at once,' agreed Idun anxiously.

'Remember to bring your own apples, Idun. We must compare the two,' Loki reminded her, and he led Idun, her apple-basket over her arm, out of Asgard, across the rainbow bridge and down into Midgard. Shortly they reached the wooded valley where Thiazi the storm giant was waiting. In his eagle's cloak, he swooped upon Idun and snatched her up, bearing her and the golden apples off to his storm-home at Thrymheim. Casting off his dark, feathered cloak, Thiazi set Idun down and grimly laughed. 'Here you'll remain, my dear.' he said. 'The gods will die, but I shall stay young forever.'

As the days passed, the gods wondered where Idun could be. While grief-stricken Bragi searched, the gods grew old and tired and withered.

At last, Odin summoned a council of the ageing gods. Loki did not attend. Heimdall, watchman of the gods, had seen Idun last. 'She was with Loki,' he announced. The hall fell silent. No one doubted now who was to blame.

'Loki must be found,' said Odin sternly.

They hunted for him throughout Asgard. It was a matter of life or death. At last they discovered Loki fast asleep in Idun's meadow, and they bound him tightly. 'Tell us where Idun is,' they said. So Loki explained how he had agreed to Thiazi's demands. 'Idun is now at his home,' he confessed.

The gods were angry, and threatened Loki. But Odin raised his hand for silence. 'We cannot blame him. But we must find a way of rescuing Idun and her apples, or we will all die.'

'The lady Freya has a falcon skin,' said Loki, eager to make amends. 'If she lends it to me, I'll fly at once to Thrymheim and try to bring Idun home.' The once-lovely Freya willingly agreed. So, swiftly, Loki set off.

When Loki reached Thrymheim, Thiazi was not there. With his keen eyes, he soon spotted pale Idun huddled beside a fire. Loki flew down, then flung off his falcon skin. 'Hold tightly to your basket,' he said. Murmuring magic words, he turned Idun and her apples into a hazelnut and himself back to a falcon. Loki picked up the hazelnut between his claws and flew off for Asgard. Before long, however, Thiazi returned home and discovered Idun's escape. Furiously he put on his eagle cloak and flew like the wind to Asgard.

Meanwhile, in Asgard, Odin and the others waited anxiously for keen-eyed Heimdall's report. At last the watchman cried, 'I see a falcon, with a hazelnut in its claws, flying this way. It is being closely chased by a black-winged eagle.'

'Bring wood and light a great fire,' shouted Odin. 'Hurry.' Flames leapt high into the air, as the eagle was almost upon the falcon, flying so fast it could not stop itself. Loki reached Asgard at last and, being the god of fire, flew unharmed through the flames with Idun safely in his claws. However, the swooping eagle's wings caught fire and it fell dead to the ground.

Loki cast off the falcon skin and grinned at the gods' anxious faces. 'Stand back,' he cried, then slowly bent over the hazelnut and spoke the magic words. There stood Idun, smiling, and her apple basket upon one arm.

Gracefully she moved among the ageing gods, giving each a golden apple, and, once they had eaten, their youth returned.

The Death of Balder

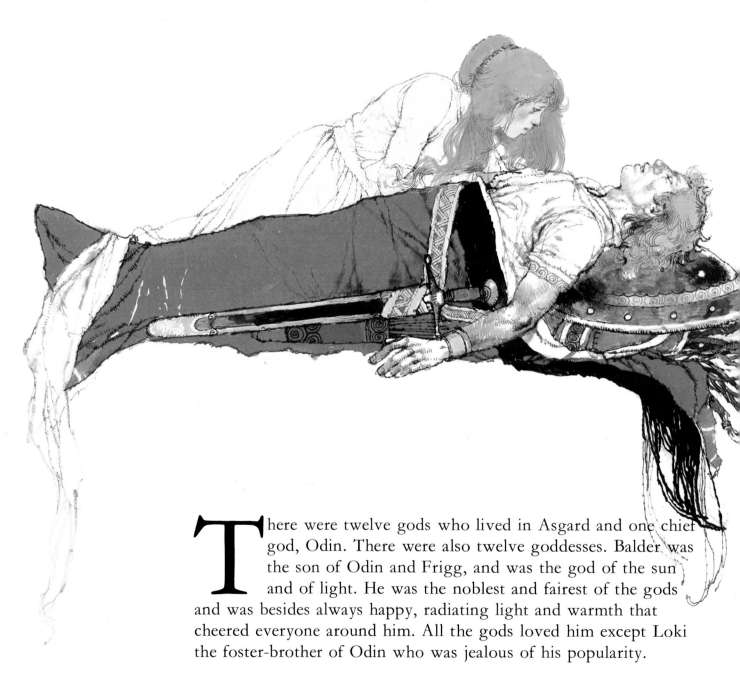

There were twelve gods who lived in Asgard and one chief god, Odin. There were also twelve goddesses. Balder was the son of Odin and Frigg, and was the god of the sun and of light. He was the noblest and fairest of the gods and was besides always happy, radiating light and warmth that cheered everyone around him. All the gods loved him except Loki the foster-brother of Odin who was jealous of his popularity.

The gods noticed one day that Balder grew pale and sad, haunted for no reason by a dream that he was going to die and no one could change his mind. So Odin called a council where it was decided that Balder's mother, Frigg, would make everything on earth swear not to harm him. That way he could be safe.

Fire took an oath; water took an oath; iron and all the other metals swore an oath. So did stone, the trees, the plants and brambles. All kinds of sickness took a vow. Each animal and bird, even the slithering snake, pledged not to harm Balder. And the gods put these vows to the test. They threw sticks and stones, iron spears and pots of water at him, but nothing could hurt Balder.

Everyone was glad that Balder could feel safe at last, everyone except Loki, the god of fire. Since fire was always jealous of light, cunning Loki longed to put out Balder's radiance, and looked for a way to harm him. So one day he disguised himself as an old woman, and visited Balder's mother Frigg. 'Tell me,' he whined, 'I saw the gods throwing stones at Balder, yet none harmed him. A most amazing sight.'

'That is because everything has sworn not to harm him,' said Frigg with a happy smile.

'You mean everything? You're sure nothing's been overlooked?'

'Well, there is the little mistletoe plant that grows in the west. It is too tiny to care about.'

Loki had learned what he wanted to know. He hurried away, took his proper shape, then went quickly to find the mistletoe. At last he found a little grove, and there, growing on the trunk of an oak-tree, he found what he was seeking: a sprig of mistletoe. Its pale berries gleamed like evil eyes. Its leaves were thin and green, its stem and twigs dull brown. Loki snapped off a sprig

Loki found a sprig of mistletoe. Its pale berries gleamed like evil eyes. Its leaves were thin and green, its stem and twigs dull brown. Loki snapped off a sprig and shaped it into a dart.

43

and shaped it into a dart. Then he returned to the gardens of the gods where they played their favourite game: throwing things at Balder, who stood there laughing and unharmed.

Only Balder's blind brother, Hod, stood apart from the others, since he could not see to aim a stone. Loki went up and poked him in the ribs. 'Why don't you throw something at your brother? It's an amusing game.'

'But I cannot see where he is,' said Hod.

'Come on, I'll help you,' Loki said. 'Here's a dart. I'll stand behind you and guide your hand.'

Hod smiled at Loki's kindness. Then, grasping the mistletoe dart, he raised his arm and aimed it, with Loki's help, at smiling Balder.

The dart flew straight and true across the green and pierced Balder through the heart. The sun-god pitched forward on to his face, killed by his brother's hand. With an evil smile, Loki stole away.

The gods' merry laughter died, and only Hod's faltering voice was heard: 'What has happened? Why does no one speak?' No one answered. The gods could not speak. They stared dumbly at the wisest, brightest, dearest of them all who lay motionless, pale as death. Slowly, their damp eyes turned to Hod, accusingly. But they knew he was not to blame. 'Who guided your aim to cause Balder's death?' one asked.

Odin gave his son Hermod, his own horse, Sleipnir, and Hermod galloped off into the darkness on the long road to Hel, the kingdom of the dead.

44

'Loki.'

Just as they thought. Of all the gods, Odin felt the greatest grief. He foresaw that a terrible disaster would follow his dear son's death. But it was Balder's mother, Frigg, who first spoke positively:

'Is there anybody here who will ride the long road to Hel, the kingdom of the dead, to rescue my son?'

At once bold Hermod, another of Odin's sons, volunteered. Odin gave him his own horse, Sleipnir, and Hermod galloped off towards the endless night.

Meanwhile, the gods carried Balder's body to the sea and laid it in his curved-prow ship, with his sword and arrows beside him. As she watched, Nanna, Balder's wife, was overwhelmed by grief. Her heart broke and she too died. So she was laid beside her husband and a funeral pyre was built.

Then, before all the assembled gods, the elves and dwarfs, the giants too—all who had come to bid farewell to the one god they all loved—Odin stepped forward with a burning torch. He lit the pyre and at once a pall of grey-blue smoke arose, twisting and billowing into the cool night air.

As the blazing ship moved slowly out to sea, the weeping throng on the shore gazed after her until she disappeared from view.

Through nine nights Hermod rode until he reached Hel. There he dismounted, walked through the gates and into the dim, cavernous hall. Countless deathly figures turned towards him, all pitiful, tormented souls.

But Hermod's eyes were fixed only on the two figures sitting together at the top of the hall: Balder and Nanna. By now Balder had lost his bright noble light; he was pale and dull. A smile of hope flitted across his face on seeing his brother, but no word of greeting passed between the two. Instead, Hermod knelt before Hel, the guardian of the dead, sitting upon her shrouded couch and eating a meal. Hel was half woman, but from the stomach down her flesh was dead: green-grey and rotting.

Hermod told Hel of the sorrow of the gods at the loss of their favourite son. 'Please, dear Hel, release my brother and let him go home.'

Hel stared right through him with her dull black eyes; her voice when she spoke was like wind howling in a graveyard. 'If everyone in the world weeps for Balder, he may return to Asgard. If not, he will remain in Hel.'

Full of hope, Hermod mounted Sleipnir and rode, unresting, until he reached Asgard. There he told the gods of Hel's grim promise. At once, the gods sent messengers to every corner of the world to ask for tears for Balder. All men and beasts wept for him. Fire and iron and every other metal wept; stones and earth and trees wept. The birds and snakes all cried their tears.

Yet as the messengers returned, thinking their task complete, they passed a cave where an ogress lived. 'Who are you?' they asked.

'Thokk is my name,' she said. So they told her of their mission and asked her, too, to weep Balder out of Hel. But she refused. 'Why should I? I have no love for him. Let Hel keep what is hers. My eyes stay dry.'

Despite their pleas, the ogress was adamant: she would not weep, she would not mourn. So the messengers returned to Asgard, defeated in their task. Balder would now remain in Hel's grasp, his life dimmed forever. And everyone knew that Thokk, the ogress, was really Loki in disguise.

The Swan of Tuonela

Early in the nineteenth century, a Finnish poet, Elias Lonnrot, set out to gather together the folk songs of Finland. Since many of the same characters turned up again and again, he felt certain that he had found sections of a lost epic or saga. After thirty years he felt that he had finished the whole saga. He called it the *Kalevala* or Land of Heroes. *The Swan of Tuonela* is just one small part of the whole to which the Finnish composer Sibelius added his moving music.

Lemminkainen came from Kalevala, land of heroes. When he was a baby, his mother had bathed him in a special way so that he grew to be a scholar and a magician, and he knew magic words. He was a dashing youth, but wild, forever teasing girls and getting into scrapes.

'It will be different when he has a wife of his own,' his mother said.

One day he told his mother, 'I am going to the north, to Pohja, to seek a bride. I shall woo the Maid of Pohja, old Louhi's eldest daughter.'

Pohja is a cold land. For one short season of the year the sun lingers in the sky and does not set. Hardy flowers blossom hastily and die; elk eat their fill of the rich grass and grow fat. Then, just as suddenly, the season is over, the year turns its face to the night, snow falls thickly on the ground and the elk move south. Each year the people follow, packing up their tents and piling their scant belongings upon the reindeer sleds. Then off they go quickly to the south.

Only old Louhi, Mistress of Pohja, stayed behind in her wooden shack with three daughters for company. The cold did not bother them. The fire burnt fiercely within the stove, yet the pile of logs remained. There was hay in the barn for cattle, and so much grain it fed the rats as well. The Mistress could wait for the sun to rise again. For she was a sorceress in the guise of a peasant woman.

'Do not go to Pohja,' Lemminkainen's mother begged. 'Choose a wife at home. Only demons and witches dwell in the north.' But Lemminkainen pulled on his padded jacket and laughed, showing his white teeth. 'I am not afraid of magic. In Pohja they sing songs to scare children; I can sing songs to frighten men.'

'Take care, my son. Old Louhi, Mistress of Pohja, is more than a match, even for heroes. Do not tangle with her.'

But Lemminkainen's mind was made up. He flung his comb into a corner of the room. 'There let my comb lie. If I die in Pohja, the comb will let you know by bleeding.' Then, taking up his sword and crossbow, he stooped to kiss his mother and stepped out of the door.

It was a hard, bitter journey of many months to Pohja. Neither man nor beast stirred between the trees; the sky was bleak. Lemminkainen had only his thoughts for company, and the whisper of his sledge's runners on the icy snow. But still he journeyed on while others moved south, until he reached Old Louhi's home.

'My journey's over, yet now the trial begins,' he said as he climbed off his sledge, stamping his feet to warm them. Suddenly two black dogs with iron teeth rushed at him. Lemminkainen did not flinch, for he had a way with dogs. Crouching on his heels, he kept stock-still and let them lick his hands. 'That's it, lads, don't bite or bark,' he said softly, fondling their ears and humming to lull them. The dogs yawned and closed their yellow eyes.

From the shack came the sound of chanting, and magic hung over his head like smoke above a fire. Inside, the Maid of Pohja, Old Louhi's eldest girl, lifted her fair head. Her keen senses warned her something was wrong. Lemminkainen shook his head and the chanting stopped. Boldly, he flung open the door. 'I come to seek your daughter as my wife,' he told Old Louhi.

'And what can you do to prove your worth?' the Mistress said.

'Set me any task, I'll gladly prove myself,' challenged Lemminkainen. The Mistress of Pohja gazed deeply into the fire. Her mind was far away, listening to the spirits. She nodded, cackled, whispered in a strange tongue; then looked up and smiled. 'Very well, you shall have your chance. You may wed my daughter if you bring me the swan of Tuonela.'

Dread gripped the young hero. 'But Tuonela is the land of the dead. No man can go there and return alive!' he shivered.

'Not even to win a bride?' asked the Mistress. 'I wish to weave my dear daughter a dress of swan's down for her wedding day. She must be worthy of you.'

'It shall be done,' said Lemminkainen gloomily. 'Tell me where to find this swan.'

'It swims upon the river of Tuonela that runs between the living and the dead,' replied Old Louhi. 'It is not far from here. Shoot the swan and you may wed my daughter.'

Lemminkainen left the Mistress's home, turned his face into the cold north wind and made for the river. Despite a swirling mist, he soon stood upon its banks. The wide river flowed slowly, save one spot where a whirlpool marked the gate of Tuonela through which all things had to pass when their time came.

Lemminkainen sat on the mist bank, unslung his cross-bow and peered across the river. 'Surely I cannot miss a swan,' he said. 'This is an easy task.' But danger neared. As he sat there unsuspecting, a poisonous water-snake, sent by Old Louhi, twisted silently through the water until it reached the reeds below Lemminkainen's feet. Then it stopped, unseen. Opening its slimy coils, it struck like lightning, then as swiftly recoiled.

Lemminkainen saw nothing, only felt the fatal bite. 'Mother,' he cried in pain, 'you taught me no charm against that sting.' And this was true for he had not learnt the words which gave protection against the bite of snakes. Quickly, the venom took its toll. Falling in the river, his dead body was pulled into the whirlpool and down, down, down to Tuonela. There, Tuoni himself, King of Tuonela, was waiting, sword in hand to destroy Lemminkainen for daring to hunt his swan.

Meanwhile, in the southlands, the months passed as Lemminkainen's mother waited. She worked the farm and made shirts for her absent son. Each day, at dawn and dusk, she looked at the fateful comb. Then, one day, she saw blood run from it. 'My son is dead,' she groaned. 'I must bring him home.'

Putting on a warm cloak, she packed her old sledge with food for the journey, and set off. At last, she reached Old Louhi's home. 'Tell me,' she said to the sorceress, 'what you have done with my son.'

'Your son wished to wed my precious daughter,' said the Mistress. 'So I sent him first to shoot the swan of Tuonela.'

For many days, Lemminkainen's mother searched along the misty river banks. She even waded into the icy flow, never thinking of her own safety, as wolves and bears came to watch. At night, she looked up hopefully at the moon. 'Moon, you see all that passes by. Have you seen my son?' But the

moon was silent. So, the year turned round and summer came. The sun thinned the mist, bringing warmth and prising open the purple and white flowers on the river bank.

'Sun, if you, perhaps, have seen Lemminkainen, please tell me where he is,' pleaded his mother, wearily.

'Old woman,' sighed the sun, 'your boy is dead, bitten by a water-snake sent by Mistress Louhi. Lemminkainen passed through Tuonela's whirlpool into the land of the dead. He has gone forever.'

'No, not forever,' said the woman. Returning to her sledge, she travelled non-stop to the forge of the hero-smith Ilmarinen and told him her story. 'Forge me a rake with brass handle and iron teeth,' she said, 'so that I may comb the river for my son.' The smith tried to dissuade her. 'I will forge you the rake you need, yet urge you not to go back.'

As he sat there, unsuspecting, a poisonous water-snake twisted silently through the water until it reached the reeds below Lemminkainen's feet. Then it stopped, unseen. Opening its slimy coils, it struck like lightning, then as swiftly recoiled.

49

She bent down tenderly
and picked up her son,
carrying him to the river
bank. 'I will bring you
back to life', she vowed.
Then she rocked on her
heels and began to sing
some magic words.

But Lemminkainen's mother would not listen. She took the rake and returned to the river of Tuonela. Once more, she called upon the sun. 'Shine with all your force upon the river and put the guardians of Tuonela to sleep, so I may rake the river-bed undisturbed.'

The sun shone down, and, wading waist-deep into the river, the old mother raked. Backwards and forwards she went, downstream and up, until the rake lay heavy in her hands, and her arms ached painfully with every sweep. But finally, she found her son's shirt. Lifting it from the water, she wrung it dry and laid it on the bank. Next, she found his hat and placed it beside his shirt. Then she found boots and other things. At last, the rake caught on Lemminkainen's body. She bent down, tenderly and picked up her son, carrying him to the river bank. 'I will bring you back to life,' she vowed. Then she rocked on her heels and began to sing some magic words. Her voice was old and thin; was there any power left? But she sang on, stroking her son and breathing life into him. At last the lady Sounetar, goddess of life, heard her and came rowing in her copper boat with its scarlet prow. She set the young hero's blood flowing through his veins once more.

Lemminkainen sat up, rubbed his eyes and stared at his mother. He was alive and healed, yet he could not speak. She held him in her arms, breathed warm breath into his lungs, sang and rubbed his throat, but it was no use. Where did speech come from? As the sun came up, a bee buzzed among the flowers nearby.

'Of course! Honey!' exclaimed Lemminkainen's mother. 'I had forgotten about the honey that even Ukka, Chief of the gods, has used as a balm.'

She caught the little bee and whispered in its ear, 'Fly away, little bee, and bring me honey.' Opening her hands, she watched the bee fly off into the sun as if meaning to take honey from Ukka's own blue meadows in the sky. After a while, the bee returned, flying slowly now, weighed down by the honey. Thanking the bee and praising the mighty Queen of Bees, the mother took the honey and smeared it on her son's cold lips, so he could lick it. No sooner had it passed his throat than he could speak again.

'Oh, mother,' the hero cried, 'you have brought me back to life. Old Louhi sent a poisonous water-snake against me and its venom took my life. Tell me, what is the charm against that poison?'

'Water-snakes come from the water where the ogress Syojatar has spat,' she said. 'Her spit is so powerful that water cannot dilute it. As lakes and rivers try to break it down, so it twists and turns until the long thread of spit becomes a snake. Next time a snake is sent against you, speak the ogress's name and it will do no harm.'

Then, together, mother and son made their way home. Lemminkainen did not win his bride but, thanks to his mother, he had regained his life. As for Old Louhi, when she heard, she screamed in fury while her snarling dogs hurled themselves the full length of their chains and bared their iron teeth. But her eldest daughter, the Maid of Pohja, sighed rather sadly, and the wind laughed in the trees.

Volund the Smith

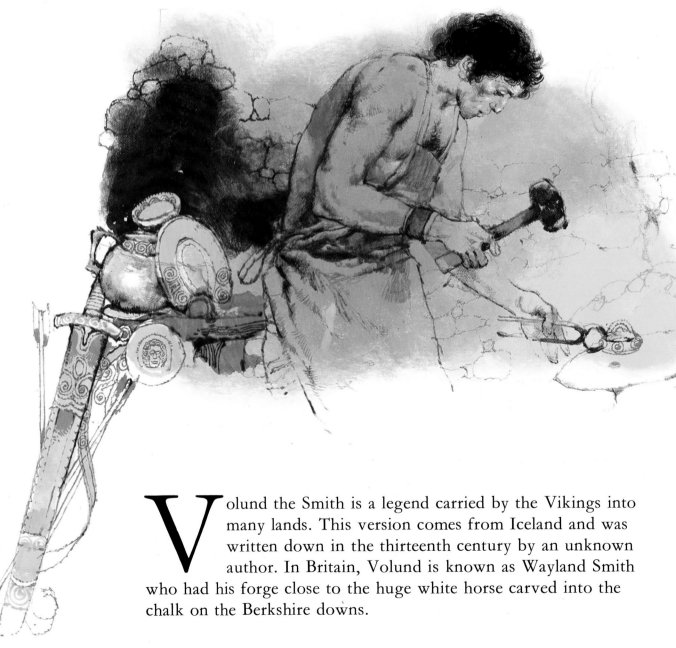

Volund the Smith is a legend carried by the Vikings into many lands. This version comes from Iceland and was written down in the thirteenth century by an unknown author. In Britain, Volund is known as Wayland Smith who had his forge close to the huge white horse carved into the chalk on the Berkshire downs.

There were once three brothers who lived beside a lake in a land far to the north. Though they were human, their veins contained a drop or two of elf blood which made them more skilled than ordinary mortal men. Two were daring hunters, and the third was a smith whose work in gold or bronze was the finest known to man. Slagfid and Egill were the hunters, Volund the smith.

Early one morning, just before dawn, the brothers awoke to the sound of soft voices coming from the lake. As they stole out of doors they found three lovely girls amidst the lilies by the lake. One was plaiting a crown of flowers, one was brushing her golden hair, one was singing softly to herself. And beside the three lay the white-feathered wings of swans.

Before the swan-maids could move, the three brothers had formed a circle around them. 'Greetings, fair maids,' said Slagfid. 'And who are you?'

The first maid with the lily crown smiled and said, 'We are Valkyries, warrior-maidens from Valhalla, where the dead heroes go. We fly where we wish on swan wings; as we are tired we are resting by this cool lake.'

'What is your name?' asked Slagfid.

'I am Hladgud.'

'I am Olrun,' said the second.

All this time, Volund had been gazing at the third maid, enchanted by her beauty and her song. 'May I know your name?' he shyly asked.

'Hervor is the name Odin gave me,' she liltingly replied. When she spoke her voice was as melodious as when she sang.

'Can you stay here long?' asked Slagfid, not wishing them to fly away.

The swan-maids looked at each other, then at the three men. 'That depends,' said Hladgud. 'Since you have welcomed us, we may stay all day.'

Volund took Hervor's hand. He so wanted the lovely girl to remain, never to fly away. 'Could you not live here for ever?' he said, his eyes telling her his love.

Hervor smiled. Then turning to her sisters she said with a sigh: 'Well, sisters, what do you say? Shall we agree?'

They whispered among themselves and it sounded like waves lapping on the shore. The brothers caught odd words: 'Weary of war . . . let's . . . peaceful lake . . . seem kind.'

It was agreed.

So the three Valkyries put aside their white-feathered wings, folding them neatly in a chest, and set up home with the men beside the lake: Hladgud with Slagfid, Olrun with Egill, Hervor, the songstress, with Volund, the smith.

For seven years the days could not be long enough, they were all so happy. But as the eighth year began, the maids grew restless for their Valhalla home, for songs from slain warriors of past battles, for the thrill of fighting and the clamour of battle. And most of all they wished to stretch their wings, to soar and swoop and hover in the air. Though their desire was strong, none of them mentioned it until one day, when the brothers were not home, the eldest sister Hladgud voiced the longing in their hearts.

'Sisters, though I love Slagfid and he is good to me, my desire to be free and see Valhalla once again is overpowering.'

Like some unblocked stream, words and tears came gushing forth. In no time at all they had opened the chest and taken out their feathered wings. They cast aside the bands that bound their hair, their smocks, the leather sandals, the braclets and other mortal gifts. And they flew off naked into the sun.

When the three brothers returned, they called the women to come and see the deer they had caught but not a sound emerged from their wooden home.

'Are they playing hide and seek with us?' laughed Egill.

'Perhaps they're ill?' said Slagfid.

Volund was silent. A strange foreboding gripped his heart; he went to the chest. He opened it slowly, hoping to see what he knew was gone, but the emptiness stared back coldly at him. There were no white wings, which meant no women, no love. From outside he heard his brothers' shouts.

'Hladgud. Olrun. Hervor! Where are you?'

'They cannot hear you. They are gone,' he said.

Volund showed them the empty chest. It made them sad, lonely, angry in turn.

'I shall seek my Hladgud wherever she may be,' cried Slagfid. 'I am a skilful tracker even in the snow.' And tying on his snow shoes he headed northwards through the snow.

'I shall go in search of my Olrun,' said Egill. 'I shall shoot my arrows in the air and bring her down.' And he tied on his snow shoes, slung a bow and quiver upon his back and trudged off eastwards through the snow.

But Volund thought to himself, 'I will wait here. Perhaps, one day Hervor will return.'

As Volund waited all alone, he made a golden ring for each day Hervor was away. Every day he worked at his anvil, hammering hard, stoking up the fire, pumping the bellows until the flames were an angry blaze, forging the molten metal with such loving care into a most beautiful ring.

As the months passed into years, a string of over seven hundred golden rings hung from the rafters in his humble home. It was like a glittering flock of birds above his head that jingled in the breeze. But the lovely Hervor did not return to claim her prize. The rings piled up and remained unworn.

Now, across the lake and beyond the distant hills, there lived a king, Nidud, who had heard stories of Volund, the finest smith in the land. Curious to see his work, the king sent out men to bring back a sample of the fabled craft: a bowl, or sword hilt or brazen plate. When the men arrived, Volund was at the lakeside, fishing. Since the door was never bolted, in case Hervor returned, the king's men entered easily, saw the string of rings, and took one for the king.

As soon as Volund came home he counted his rings, which he did each day, and found one missing. His heart beat faster as he thought that Hervor was home at last. But it was not to be. Disappointed, he set to work at once to forge another ring.

Meanwhile, King Nidud was astounded at the workmanship in the golden ring. Certainly, no other smith in all his realm had such skill. He was so delighted that he gave it to his only daughter Bodvild, whom he loved above all else. She was so thrilled at the splendid present that she wished for more gifts made by the smith.

Volund the Smith

They cast aside the bands that bound their hair, the homespun smocks, the leather sandals, the bracelets and other mortal gifts. And they flew off naked into the sun.

'You shall have your wish, my child,' her father said. And he sent his men once more to the lakeside shack, this time to fetch the smith himself. Despite his huge strength, poor Volund was seized and bound and dragged off to the king.

'You are a noble craftsman,' said the king. 'Did you alone make my daughter's ring?'

'I made no ring for her or any other viper in your nest!' Volund angrily exclaimed. He was mad with rage at seeing the ring he had made for Hervor worn by someone else. 'Give me back that ring,' he roared, struggling with his bonds. He managed to break half-free, knocked down several men, and would have strangled the frightened monarch had not a host of guards quickly held him down.

'This savage beast needs taming,' said the king. 'I will make him work for me forging rich swords and jewellery.'

'I will work for no one,' cried Volund, 'least of all for thieving brigands like you.'

'I have an idea,' said the queen. 'Why don't we cripple him and set him on the isle of Saevarstad? Then he will not be able to flee.'

'What an excellent idea,' her husband said with an evil smile.

The two royal princes came to watch the cruel show, jeering at Volund's pain. When the job was done, Volund could only hobble in agony. He was

'I have an idea', said the queen. 'Why don't we cripple him, then he will not be able to flee.' When the job was done, Volund could only hobble in agony.

taken in a boat to the isle of Saevarstad, a stone's throw from the shore, where he was left with only a hut and forge.

Each day, gold and precious stones were ferried across to the island with the king's instructions on what he wanted to be made: knives, gold cups, brooches and rings.

If Volund refused, he had no food or drink. And since he still hoped to see his beloved Hervor once again, he had no choice but to do as he was ordered. But a bitter hatred burned within him for the cruel king. One day he determined to take revenge upon the man.

Then an idea came to him, an idea so daring it could surely not come true. Since he could not walk, he would make a pair of wings and fly away. Surely it was worth a try.

He gathered feathers left by birds, wood flotsam cast up by the tide, and brass filings left over from his toil. Every night, when the royal work was done, he set about his daring task.

But one night, in the middle of his work, he had a visit from the two royal sons. Being as greedy as their father, they had secretly rowed across to steal their father's gold. They almost caught Volund working on his wings, but luckily for him their minds were on other matters.

'We shall not harm you, lame man,' they said. 'We have come to take our father's gold. No one knows we're here.'

Smiling to himself, Volund willingly led them to a wooden chest in the corner of his forge. 'Take all you want,' he said, 'it is all the same to me.' But inwardly he thought, 'Now my revenge begins.'

As he had guessed, the two princes soon fell out, quarrelling over the division of the spoils. They were too busy to notice the smith creeping up behind them with an axe.

Swish! Their heads rolled across the floor.

Volund buried their bodies beneath the forge, then he made two goblets from the bone of their skulls, set in silver. Out of their teeth, he fashioned a brooch set in gold for the princess. And from their eyes, he made four amber-set pendants for the queen.

The king received the presents gratefully, not knowing what they were. No one missed the royal pair since they were often away hunting for weeks on end. Meanwhile, Volund continued with his task, fashioning his wings by the light from the fire. He was almost finished when the princess Bodvild broke the ring her father had given her from Volund's home. Fearing her father's anger, she slipped away to Saevarstad to seek the smith's skilled help.

'Does anyone know you've come?' Volund asked anxiously.

'No, I came secretly. My ring is broken. Will you mend it for me?'

When Volund saw Hervor's ring he almost killed Bodvild on the spot. But he restrained himself and asked her in. She was half-frightened of the crippled man, for she had heard stories of his elf blood and wild ways. And yet he seemed so kind, youthful and handsome. A wave of pity and admiration overcame her fear: pity for the lonely fate her father had inflicted on him, and admiration for his courage and his skill. Little did she know what fate had planned for her.

Volund looked up, and saw the girl, her golden hair burnished in the fiery glow, her cheeks flushed by mead and flame.

'Sit here and drink a cup of mead,' Volund said, his blue eyes smiling kindly, 'while I mend the ring.'

Leaving her for a moment, he went out to fetch his axe. Yet first he felt impelled to mend the ring. 'My beloved Hervor first,' he mused. 'I'll deal with the king's child in a moment.'

The mead was strong, the cup was deep, and the girl thought it impolite to refuse the drink. So she drained the cup and then, emboldened, rose and stood watching the figure lit up by the blazing fire. Sweat made his muscles glow and tears smudged his sun-tanned face, but she didn't know why. His sad thoughts were far away and he didn't notice the eyes upon him.

'Volund,' she called softly.

The sound made him jump. He looked up, and saw the girl, her golden hair burnished in the fiery glow, her cheeks flushed by mead and flame. His hardened heart softened a little.

'Volund, I would willingly remain with you if you would let me,' she said.

He stared at her, still numbed by his long suffering and pain, but partly thawed by her gentle innocence.

'I am not to blame for what my father has done,' she said, sensing his unspoken hate. 'I hate my parents for what they have done to you. If I had to choose, I would give my love to you, not them.'

Volund took her hands in his. 'Bodvild, I have no more anger in my heart for you. But I cannot return your love. You see, I once loved a swan-maid,

Hervor, who has flown away. Soon I shall leave to seek her. I forgive you; please pardon me.'

As she turned to go, head bowed to hide her tears, he held her arm. 'Here, take this ring to remind you of your love,' and he slipped Hervor's ring upon her finger. Then he limped painfully to the water's edge to say goodbye and she rowed silently back to shore.

All that night Volund worked hard upon his wings and by dawn they were ready: supple and strong. Carrying them to a mound in the centre of the island, he strapped them on and waited for a breeze. Then, pushing himself off he rose gently off the ground, flapped once, twice, and floated on the wind. Up and away, across the sea and above the nearby shore. There he landed on the high, arched gate of King Nidud's great hall, and cried out loudly for the king.

When Nidud and the queen came out to see what had made the strange, yet somehow familiar sound, they could not believe their eyes. There stood the smith, high above them, attached to wooden wings tipped with feathers and bound with brass.

'Where are your sons, King Nidud?' shouted Volund.

'They must be lost, somewhere in the forest,' the king said warily.

'Look beneath the floor of my forge,' Volund said. 'You'll find their rotting bones. And where's your daughter, Queen?'

'She sits and weeps and says she hates us. Someone has turned her head,' the queen replied.

Volund gave a harsh laugh. 'Now I have punished you for your cruelty. For you have lost your sons and your daughter's love.'

The queen shrieked in horror, and the king roared in pain and called to his archers to shoot Volund down. But he spread his wings and flew away, his laughter drifting back on the wind.

Volund the mighty smith flew on and up above the clouds, right across the world. He was heading for Valhalla to be re-united with his swan-maiden.

Why the Tribes Speak Different Tongues

Australians owe a debt to white Australians of the last century for preserving the cultural heritage of the original Australians, the Aborigines. The remnants of legends salvaged by them can tell us little of the realities of which they were part. But for modern readers it is interesting to note that although some of the elements in the stories may be lost the essential truths are as true today as they ever were.

Thhere was a time when all the tribes spoke a single tongue. So a stranger was always understood and no-one stumbled over foreign words, or was thought foolish in the silence which comes when people cannot speak to one another. Thus, ideas passed easily between the many tribes, and friendship bound them.

As time passed, however, the marriage laws preventing women of one tribe marrying the men of another caused discontent. And the elders met and made a new law: members of all tribes could intermarry. A Dingo woman could marry a Goanna man; a Kangaroo man could wed an Emu woman; and so on. Yet some tribes were angry at this change of law. They opposed the ruling of the elders and sharpened their spears. These people were mainly from the Tortoise, the Frog and Crow tribes, and they spoke up because there were too many men to go round; so some would have no wives.

To avoid unrest, the elders called a meeting of all the tribes to discuss the matter. But those who favoured change did not want a meeting, unlike the Tortoise, Frog and Crow. Knowing them to be warlike, the other tribes armed themselves ready for attack. They brought their boomerangs, their nulla-nullas and spears, and they waited at the meeting place for trouble. But men of the Tortoise, Frog and Crow were not foolish; their numbers were small, so they decided upon a plan. They would wear the others out until they could have their way.

On the day of the arranged meeting, the Tortoise, Frog and Crow tribes started to dance. When one tribe tired, another took over. They pounded the earth, shouting and did not stop even to eat. Meanwhile, the watching tribes did not dare leave the corroboree ground as long as the dancing went on, for that would bring bad luck. So their hunger increased, their eyelids grew heavy and their heads began to swim. For three long days the Tortoise, the Frog and the Crow danced. And on the third, the hunger and weariness of all those who watched turned to anger and bitterness. It led to harsh words, men struck their brothers, women their friends. The single language ensured everyone understood the insults that were shouted. Anger turned to rage and fighting broke out. That day, many died and, afterwards, the tribes went their separate ways, full of hate. Then each tribe agreed to speak its own language so all that was said was for its people, alone. That is how it is today.

Not long after the tribes had fallen out, a strange thing happened to the land: all the flowers upon the plains and hills, and the blossoms on the trees withered and died. None grew in their place. The brown earth looked bare and parched. That was the punishment for the tribes fighting.

As the years passed, the children grew up never having seen a flower, and so such things became mere memories in the folk tales of the old ones. Since the blossoms were gone, so too were the bees. In vain the men searched and the women took out their bark dishes to fill with honey. Throughout the land there was not a bee to be found. Children cried for something to sweeten their food and mothers murmured because the wirinuns, the wise men, could not work their magic.

At last the All-Seeing Spirit took pity on the tribes. Although he was still angry over their feuding, he decided to send them food as sweet as the taste of

Flowers grew everywhere. They were such bright colours, that it was like hundreds of rainbows shining in the grass.

honey. Soon the people noticed white specks of sugar on the leaves of the bibbil and coolabah trees; then came clear manna running down the trees like honey. It stiffened on the forks of branches and gathered in lumps upon the trunk. The children gathered it and ate gratefully, and for a time the people were happy again. Yet stories of the day when flowers adorned the earth stirred up a longing in young and old alike. They wished to see the earth bloom and so great was their desire that they sent a band of wirinuns, one man from each tribe, towards the north-east to find the All-Seeing Spirit.

On and on they travelled, until they finally reached the foot of the great Oobi-Oobi Mountain, which towered high above them, vanishing into the cloudy sky. As they walked around the mountain they saw its sides were steep and smooth; nowhere could they find a foothold. At last, they came upon a ledge cut into the sheer rock, then more, until they saw a series of stone steps which they began to climb. Up and up they went, but at the end of the first day the mountain top seemed as far away as ever. It was the same on the second and third days, for the steps led round the mountain and not straight up. On the fourth day, though, they suddenly emerged on to the summit, above the clouds. At first, the men were so tired, they could not move. Then they drank thirstily from a natural spring and, strangely, their weariness faded.

As they sat round the freshwater spring, they noticed nearby a circle of stones. Edging uncertainly into it, they heard the sound of the gayandi, or bull-roarer, through which came the voice of Walla-guroon-bu-an, the spirit messenger of the All-Seeing Spirit. He asked the wirinuns what they were seeking; for this was the place where the sacred lore was told to those who came in search of knowledge. Eagerly they explained how dull and dreary the earth looked without flowers, tree blossom or the little bees that had once provided honey. 'Though the Great Spirit has sent us manna', they said, 'we long for honey and flowers to make the land sweet and bright again.' Then Walla-guroon-bu-an ordered other invisible spirits to lift the wirinuns up into Bullima, the sky camp, where there were unfading flowers and always blossom in the trees.

'Gather as many blossoms as you can hold,' he told the men of the tribes, 'and take them back to your people.' As the voice faded, unseen hands lifted the wirinuns through an opening in the sky, and set them down in a land of amazing beauty. Flowers grew everywhere. They were such bright colours, it was like hundreds of yulu-wirrees, or rainbows, shining in the grass. The men cried for joy. Then they stooped to collect armfuls of the different-coloured blossoms. In a few moments they were lifted up again, along with their flowers, and returned through the opening in the sky to the ground within the stone circle. There they heard the voice of the gayandi, and Walla-guroon-bu-an said, 'Tell your tribes that as long as they do not fight they shall have these flowers. Throughout the seasons, blooms shall be sent by the different winds. Yarraga Mayra, the east wind, shall bring blossoms in spring to every tree and bush, to wave among the grasses, as thick as hairs upon the possum's back.

'But in autumn and inter,' continued Walla-guroon-bu-an, 'when flowers are few and the sweet-breathed wind does not blow and the bees cannot make their honey, the manna shall again drop from trees until the rains come to open blossoms for the bees. So the land will be sweet all year round. Now make haste and take these flowers back to your people.'

As the voice faded the wirinuns made their way down the mountain by the same stone steps, taking the Bullima flowers to their tribes. When they reached the plains, the people crowded about them, staring in wonder. The flowers filled the air with their sweet scent, as fresh as when they grew in Bullima.

After the tribes had gazed for a long time at the blossoms and heard of the words of Walla-guroon-bu-an, the wirinuns scattered the flowers far and wide. Some were swept up by the wind and dropped on tree tops, some on plains and ridges, the woggis and morillas; and where they fell they have blossomed ever since.

The spot where the wirinuns first scattered the flowers is still called Girraween, place of flowers. There, after the bees had caused the east wind to blow rain down the Oobi-Oobi Mountain to soften the frosty ground, green grass and bright flowers appeared, and the trees and bushes blossomed.

But the tribes well know that if they should fight again, the land would once more turn to dust and they would never see the bright flowers and bees.

The Love Story of Hine-moa

The Polynesians are the native people of many islands in the Pacific. It is an ocean world and their mythology and stories are aptly known as Oceanic mythology. Among the peoples in Oceania are the Maoris, the native inhabitants of New Zealand; the Tahitians, Samoans and all the peoples of the neighbouring islands. Their myths and legends are all similar and many, as in the story of Hine-moa, are centred around the oceans.

Like the stories of many other peoples of Africa and Asia, Maori myths and legends have been collected and written down almost entirely by literate men of another culture and religion. Despite the obvious dangers of distortion, the Polynesian literature amassed is vast and rich.

Since the beginning of time, as the waves roll and break upon the courtyard of the sea, the ocean maid Hine-moana and her husband Kiwa, guardian of the sea, have ruled the waters of bay, inlet, lake and stream that wash the earth. Their realm is called Te Moana-nui-a-Kiwa. And the many wave-children which Hine-moana wraps in shell and seaweed for protection, are a sign of the great love between herself and Kiwa.

The stories of the strong ocean maid are matched by those of Maori women who have swum great distances in the cold lakes of the southern islands. There is Hine-poupou. She is the only person to have battled through the waves across Cook Strait, to escape from Kapiti Island where her unfaithful husband had marooned her. There is Te Rau-o-te-rangi, who swam with her baby on her back from Kapiti to Waikanae to escape her enemies. And Rau-whato who swam five miles across the freezing waters from the northern shore of Lake Taupo, with her child tied to her back. And there is Hine-moa whose love was stronger than the cold, surging waters.

On the banks of Lake Rotorua, at Owhata, Hine-moa had grown to womanhood, strong-limbed and graceful, the delight and pride of her mother Hine-maru and father Umi-karia. She was of noble birth, descended from the founder of the Ngati-umu-karia tribe. So the young woman of Owhata was famed far and wide as a fitting bride for only the noblest of men.

In the middle of Lake Rotorua was the island of Mokoia where a young man named Tutanekai lived with his mother and elder brothers. Tutanekai was the son of Rangi-uru, wife of Whakaue-kaipapa. Once, Rangi left her husband to run off with a warrior and Tutanekai was their son. Later she returned, bringing Tutenekai with her. Whakaue welcomed them, though the boy was sometimes taunted by his elder brothers.

Since the tribes of Hine-moa and Tutanekai were at peace, they often visited each other. One day, the young men of Mokoia prepared to row across to Owhata to take part in ceremonial dances called hakas and in games. Shy young Tutanekai went, too. Before setting off, they gathered presents for the girls: the ripe fruit of the miro to make sweet oil, herbs and grasses for scent.

A great crowd gathered to watch, and the dancers stood waiting in ranks. First came the steady stamping of the young men of Owhata; behind them the women, led by Hine-moa rushed forward, her eyes wide and her body twisting in a dance of welcome.

As he watched Hine-moa, Tutanekai's heart beat faster and he knew, from that moment, he would never love anyone else.

As if to tease Tutanekai, Hine-moa jumped up and down, poking out her tongue, then hurried behind the other dancing girls. Yet, in that brief moment, love kindled between them. But, no word was spoken, for they were both young and shy.

After returning home, Tutanekai built himself a hut high on the hillside, so he could gaze across the lake towards Owhata. In the cool of evening he would sit and play his flute, and sometimes, when the wind was right, the notes floated on the breeze to the ears of Hine-moa, making her heart pound.

Tutanekai was too shy to declare his love for Hine-moa. But after he had met her several times at gatherings in Owhata, he pressed her hand once and

On the banks of Lake Rotorua, Hine-moa grew to womanhood. She was strong-limbed and graceful, the delight and pride of her mother and father.

felt a faint response. At last, unable to bear things any more, he sent a messenger–such was the custom in those days–to tell her of his love. When Hine-moa heard the news, she simply sighed, 'Eh hu! Our love, then, is one.' And the answer came back to Tutanekai.

There was now an urgent note of longing in Tutanekai's music that drifted across the lake on calm nights. Then just after sundown one night at the meeting-house on Mokoia, the sons of Rangi and Whakaue began to talk of Hine-moa. 'Has anyone proof that Hine-moa returns their love?' one asked. 'I have,' several cried at once, claiming they had squeezed her hand.

'And you, Tutanekai?'

'I have pressed her hand and felt the pressure of hers on mine,' he said. 'And I have seen love for me in her eyes.' His brothers laughed. 'You're imagining things, Tutanekai. How could a noble maid notice you?'

His eyes filled with angry tears. 'I do have proof Hine-moa loves me,' he cried. 'What's more, when we were together last night she said she would come here to me the moment I gave a sign. I told her that on a calm night she would hear my flute across the lake and would know it was the melody of love. Then she will take a small canoe and paddle it to me here.'

'Where is she then?' his brothers continued to jeer. 'We hear your love notes every night, but see no small canoe.' And late into the night, they mocked and teased Tutanekai.

Just as she thought she could not go on, she reached a half-sunken tree stump. It was a welcome resting place which certainly saved her life. Hine-moa clung to it, trying to regain her strength.

Night after night, Tutanekai stood upon the porch of his hillside hut, playing his flute. But there was never a sign of Hine-moa's canoe. He had no way of knowing that her family had noticed Hine-moa's love-struck face whenever she heard the flute and had dragged the canoes well up the beach so she could not move them by herself.

What was she to do? When she stood by the lakeside, listening to the faint song drifting across the water, she felt as if the ocean maid herself was telling her to swim to Tutanekai. It was a long way from Owhata to Mokoia, but in the lonely sadness of the night, Hine-moa decided to try. She slipped off her clothes, took six dried gourds and tied three to each side of her, to help her float. Then, stepping on to the rock of Wai-rere-wai, above the lake, she dived into the dark, cold waters. Her strong will helped to give her strength. There was no moon, so no one would see Hine-moa who hoped the sound of Tutanekai's flute would guide her. For what seemed an age she battled through the waves, until her aching arms and legs could hardly move. Just as she thought she could not go on, she reached a half-sunken tree stump known as Hine-whata. It was a welcome resting place which certainly saved her life. Hine-moa clung to it, trying to regain her strength. But the bitter-cold water chilled her through, making her tremble. At that moment, the music from Tutanekai's flute brought her new hope and fresh strength. She swam on again, till at last she reached shallow water and felt firm rock beneath her feet. Just then, the music stopped. It was late, and Tutanekai prepared to sleep. Meanwhile, down on the beach, beyond his hut, there was a warm-water pool known as Waikimihia, though now called Hine-moa's Pool. Wearily and shivering with cold, Hine-moa lowered herself thankfully into it.

Presently, she heard footsteps on the sand. Tutanekai's servant approached the pool to fill his calabash with water. Hine-moa spoke to him quietly. 'Who is the water for?' The servant jumped, then stammered 'For Tutanekai.'

'Give me the calabash,' said Hine-moa. A hand reached out of the darkness, took the bowl and smashed it against the rocks. Terrified, the servant raced back to tell his master of the evil spirit hidden in the pool. Angrily Tutanekai threw on a cloak, seized a stick and ran down the hillside. 'Where is the man who broke my calabash?' he shouted, as he approached the pool. 'Come out, so I can see you.'

When Hine-moa heard Tutanekai's voice, she hid under the rocks overhanging the pool. Her heart was beating fast and she longed to take him in her arms, but she was shy. Still angry, Tutanekai felt his way round the edge of the pool until he touched a hand. 'Ah-ha, caught you! Now come out.' So Hine-moa stepped from her hiding place and stood before him. 'It is I, Hine-moa.' Tutanekai could hardly believe it. Wrapping Hine-moa in his cloak, they climbed the hillside together.

Next morning, as the villagers sat at breakfast, Whakaue suddenly noticed that Tutanekai was missing. 'He must have overslept, father,' said another son. 'It's unlike him. Someone had better go and wake him up. Perhaps he's ill.' When a boy was sent to look, he soon returned shouting; 'It's Hine-moa.'

There was uproar. 'Impossible! She could not have got here,' amazed voices cried.

Angrily, Tutanekai threw on a cloak, seized a stick and ran down the hillside. 'Where is the man who broke my calabash?' he shouted.

But as Hine-moa and Tutanekai approached, everyone saw it was true. Some of Tutanekai's brothers were jealous. Why should Hine-moa choose him? Yet their moans were drowned by a shout of welcome from all the others.

And since Hine-moa had chosen her husband, her family did not object. They welcomed Tutanekai and the tribes were bound more tightly in friendship than before.

To this day the descendants of Hine-moa and Tutanekai, who live by Lake Rotorua, still tell the story of love in verse and song. And the girls gladly demonstrate their powerful swimming skills.

Rama and Sita

The *Ramayana* from which this story is taken is one of the two great epics of India, the other being the much longer *Mahabharata*. This story comes from the early days of the Aryan occupation of northern India and, after being woven into legend, it was shaped into its present form by Valmiki in the fourth century BC. This version was learned by heart and recited all over India until it was written down in Sanskrit, in the late sixteenth century.

The *Ramayana* is as much a religious teaching to Hindus as is the New Testament to Christians. Rama and Sita are the ideal man and woman, examples to all Indian boys and girls; and many are named after them. So the story is a vital part of Indian life and culture.

The gods gathered in sadness in the high courts of heaven, for their chief enemy Ravana, prince of demons, roamed the three worlds, sometimes fighting the gods and disturbing the air, earth and waters. Yet Brahma, creator of the worlds, had once granted Ravana a favour that no god or demon could ever kill him. So how could they put an end to his evil? Finally, they agreed on a plan. They would give heavenly food to the king of Koshala for his three wives. This meant that the children of each wife would have some of the nature of a god. Then the gods would choose one of the sons to fight Ravana for them, as he was not protected from men.

In the spring the queens had their sons. First born, was the child of the queen who had eaten half the heavenly food. He was named Rama, the 'joy' of his parents and the world. A few days later a son was born to the second queen and called Bharata, the 'guardian' of the kingdom. Then the third wife gave birth to twin boys, Lakshmana, the 'fortunate', and Shatrughna, the 'victor'.

The boys were all strong and handsome. Rama and Bharata were as dark as storm clouds, the twins were fairer, but all had dark curly hair and eyes as wide as lotus leaves, black and bright. And they all learned wisdom, and skill with the bow and sword. Rama was always best, for he was the eldest and possessed half the nature of a god.

One day, when the boys were fifteen years old, a wise man came to the king with a strange request. 'Lend me your son Rama for a while to fight some demons sent by Ravana, for Rama is chosen by the gods.'

Not daring to offend the holy-man, the king agreed, but also sent his son Lakshmana to keep Rama company. Carrying their swords and quivers, the boys followed the man out of the city and along a river-bank. After several adventures, they came to the city of King Janaka. Now the king owned a rare and wonderful bow given him by the gods, and he told the young princes about it saying, 'Though many have tried, no man can even lift it, let alone string the bow. If either of you can string it, I will give my daughter Sita in marriage. Though I call her my daughter, she was not born of mortals. Some years ago, in spring I was ploughing land when I opened a furrow and found a baby lying in the soil. I brought her home and she has grown up as my daughter. I named her Sita, the 'furrow', since she is the daughter of the Earth, goddess of spring. And I decided that no ordinary man should marry her, only one who could bend the mighty bow.'

The bow was carried in by twelve men. Rama stepped forward, grasped it at the centre and easily lifted it. Then, resting one end against his foot and using all his strength, he bent it towards himself to string it. As he did so, it gave an almighty crack like a thunderbolt that echoed far and wide. 'The bow is strung!' cried many voices. King Janaka was delighted, gladly giving Sita in marriage to Rama. At the ceremony, Rama took his bride's hand, walked three times round a fire and the wedding was complete.

For twelve years, Sita and Rama, with his brother, Lakshmana, lived happily at the court of King Janaka. Then, once more, the wise man came to Rama, saying 'Rama, you must go into the forest, wearing hermit's clothing and live on fruit and roots. That is your next trial.'

'If it is my fate, I will do it,' said Rama. Since his wife and brother would

Sita, dressed in her
yellow sari and with her
lovely black hair hanging
loose, sat weeping on a
carpet of leaves inside the
safety of the circle.

not desert him, the three set off together, following the route the wise man had told them: 'Towards the meeting of the rivers Jumna and the Ganges, then on through the jungle until you reach a hermitage among the trees, far from the nearest village.' Rama, Sita and Lakshmana grew used to their jungle life and were happy there together. They bathed each day in the bright waters of the river and gathered lotus blossoms and water lilies, while cranes and wild geese fished in the shallows. They walked among the trees, finding cool caves and flowering glades. They sought out the finest fruit trees–fig, mango, breadfruit and banana–and collected honey and berries for food. Sometimes the two brothers shot a deer or antelope, and used the soft skins to cover their beds and make warm garments. They also speared fish which they cooked on a fire.

Meanwhile Ravana, the demon king, heard of the brothers and Sita. So one day he made himself invisible, and went to see them. He was struck by Sita's beauty and wanted her for himself. So he devised a plan. He sent his servant Maricha to the jungle, disguised as a small deer. Its hide was of gold, dappled with silver, its horns were tipped with gems that glittered in the sunlight, and its tiny hoofs were encased in emerald.

The deer wandered into a glade by the hermitage, nibbling at leaves, bounding across the grass, and Sita soon saw it. Quietly, so as not to scare the deer, she called to Rama. 'O Rama, what a sweet little deer. Catch it for me, please; I want it for a pet. Or if you cannot, then shoot it and bring me its golden hide.'

Eager to please his wife, Rama left Lakshmana to guard Sita, took his bow and crept towards the deer. But it sprang off into the trees, then stopped, as if waiting until Rama went closer. Then away it ran again, luring him ever farther from his home. Rama soon realized he would never catch the deer so, fixing an arrow to his bow, he fired at it. The deer leapt into the air then fell. But as it died, it called in Rama's own voice, 'Save me, Sita, save me!' Rama was amazed, and also alarmed at what Sita might think.

'It is Rama,' cried Sita as she heard. 'He must be in danger. Lakshmana, go to him at once.' Lakshmana was torn between his concern for Rama and his duty to guard Sita. But eventually, after Sita pleaded tearfully, he ran off in the direction from which the cry had come. Before he left, he used a stick to draw a circle on the ground and told Sita to stay within it. Then she would be safe from demons. But no sooner had Lakshmana gone, than Ravana emerged from the trees. He was disguised as a Brahman, a priest, dressed in a saffron robe, bearing a begging bowl and leaning on a staff. Immediately, the breeze dropped, leaves hung motionless, birds stopped singing and even the river ceased to flow. Sita, dressed in her yellow sari and with her lovely black hair hanging loose, sat weeping on a carpet of leaves inside the circle.

'Will you give me food, dear lady?' asked a gentle voice. It startled her. Yet when she saw the Brahman, her fears faded. 'Come to the hut,' she said. 'I'll gladly give you food and wash your feet.'

'I cannot move another step,' replied the feeble voice. 'I am weak and tired from hunger'. Then he fell to the ground.

Taking pity, Sita hurried to help him . . . and left the safety of the circle. In a moment, Ravana threw off his disguise and, seizing her in his powerful arms,

'Rama cannot save you', laughed the demon king.

he carried her off to his chariot pulled by golden-headed mules. As it rose into the air, Sita screamed Rama's name while she struggled desperately. But up and up flew the chariot, speeding over forests, rivers, mountains and lakes. Meanwhile, Sita cried out to the trees, river, sun, deer and even the great vulture Jatayu to tell Rama what had happened.

As they crossed a hill, she pulled off her veil and dropped it, to alert five monkeys sitting on the hilltop. She hoped they too might tell Rama. On flew the chariot, over the ocean to Ravana's kingdom on the island of Lanka. 'Rama cannot save you,' laughed the demon king. 'I lead ten-thousand demons, and each has a thousand servants. Not even the gods can take my island. So now, fair one, you are mine.' Sita trembled like an aspen leaf, but she was more angry than afraid. 'I belong to Rama,' she cried then covered her face with her robe and wept. 'My husband and his brother will come. You cannot be killed by god or demon, but you will not escape when Rama attacks.'

The demon king sneered coldly before he summoned the slaves who guarded all his wives. 'Take this woman to the ashoka grove and guard her well' he ordered. And there, overcome by despair, Sita fainted.

Back in the forest, Rama had quickly set off home. But he met his brother on the way. 'Why have you abandoned Sita?' he asked. 'The voice that cried out was demon's doing.' Lakshmana explained how Sita had begged him to go, and about the circle he had drawn for her. But, uneasily, the two brothers ran to the hermitage to find it empty, the blossoms dead, the mat and deerskins scattered everywhere. Sita was nowhere to be seen. They searched everywhere, calling her name. But it was no use. 'Demons must have taken her,' said Rama. 'We must find her. Surely someone saw her go.'

They talked to the sun, moon and wind, to the trees, animals and fish. Yet only the deer, who loved Sita, approached and used their heads to point south as they looked up. Then they wandered off as if urging both brothers to follow. As the two men pursued, Lakshmana spotted some blossoms on the ground. 'Look, Rama. You gave these to Sita this morning for her hair. We are on the path she took.' Farther on they found a broken necklace, and then heard a voice above them in the trees; it was Jatayu, the mighty vulture. 'The demon king Ravana has taken Sita to his kingdom on the island of Lanka, in the south. She asked me to tell you. I know no more.'

So the brothers continued their journey until, after several months, they reached Lake Pampa. It was late spring and the water was calm and beautiful, bordered by trees as lofty as hills. Waterfowl swam on the lake, while deer and elephants came to drink. As Rama and Lakshmana rested, Sugriva, the monkey king, watched them from his hilltop home, guarded by four faithful servants. He sent one to fetch the brothers. 'I can help you find your wife,' he told Rama. Sugriva explained all he knew and showed him the veil which Sita had dropped. When he saw it, Rama wept. 'I shall send a monkey army to travel with you to Ravana's island fortress,' said Sugriva, 'and my most trusted friend Hanuman, son of the wind god, will help you too.'

The expedition, led by Hanuman, sped southwards. The monkeys were excited and hopeful. They longed to be free from Ravana as he had tormented them too. They travelled through forests and barren land until they finally reached a mountain, towering above the raging sea. Rama stared gloomily at the deep, wild waters, full of ocean monsters. 'Listen, Rama,' began Hanuman, 'Ravana lives in Lanka, a city built by the gods. We must build a bridge across the ocean to reach the island. I will fetch Nala, son of the gods' architect who built Lanka itself. He has his father's skill.' Nala came forward, pressed the palms of his hands together in greeting and agreed what was asked. First, he had the entire mountainside pulled down. Its trees and rocks were used to form the bridge's foundations, while stones and earth filled the cracks. The monkeys rushed about, carrying materials and becoming increasingly excited as the bridge approached the shore of the island.

Finally, it was done and so the whole army began to cross it, with Rama, Lakshmana and Hanuman leading the way. By morning, every monkey was on the shore, ready to march on the city. Soon they approached its mighty walls and each monkey captain led his battalion to the appointed gate. Then they all waited for the signal to attack, while the amazed demons looked down terrified. At Rama's command, the monkeys in their thousands rushed the walls and tried to break down the city gates. But Ravana ordered his demon troops to counter-attack. Amid the sound of drums, trumpets and a blast from conch shells, they poured from the gates on chariots and elephants, clad in armour and gripping their spears.

A great battle followed. The monkeys shouted, 'Victory to Rama!' the demons, shouted 'Glory to Ravana!' Although better armed, the demons soon began to retreat. So Ravana himself rushed into battle with all his demon fury, firing flaming arrows and hurling a spear hung with eight loud bells. It winged its way towards Lakshmana, striking him down.

They heard a voice above them in the trees; it was Jatayu, the mighty vulture.

Rama was grief-stricken when he saw his brother fall. He lunged at Ravana and a furious struggle began. Wise in the ways of warfare, both had weapons made by the gods; neither had ever known defeat. As they circled one another, the adversaries fired arrows, but they could not pierce each fighter's impenetrable armour. In a half-circle behind Rama, the monkeys cheered him. So too did the demons support their king.

Meanwhile, from on high, the gods also watched, for they had planned this long ago, and their own safety from Ravana depended on who won. As both assailants began to tire, Rama made one last effort. Taking out his final arrow, he fixed it to his bow and muttered magic words. Then, with his last remaining strength, he fired. Hissing through the air like a winged snake, the arrow passed clean through Ravana and returned to Rama's hand. The demon king crashed to the ground. When they saw him lying lifelessly, his followers fled, pursued by the monkeys shouting and chattering in triumph. Lakshmana, restored to life by healing herbs, joined his brother. Then, together, they hurried with Hanuman to find Sita. Was she still alive?

When they discovered she was safe, Sita would have run into her beloved husband's arms but for a strange expression on his face. Indeed, everyone noticed the change that suddenly came over him. Rama's face was clouded and frowning, his voice cold. 'I have killed my enemy,' he said to Sita, 'and rescued you. Now go where you please. I cannot take you back for I feel I cannot trust you. Ravana's evil gaze has rested on you.' Sita listened in disbelief, her eyes filling with tears. Never before had she heard Rama speak unkindly and his cruel words pierced her like arrows. She hid her face and wept bitterly. Then she wiped her eyes and looked at Rama proudly. 'Why do you say this? It was not my fault Ravana captured me. What could I do? My heart has always been yours.'

Turning to Lakshmana, she continued, 'Build a fire. I speak the truth, the flames will not harm me.' As Rama looked away, Lakshmana grimly kindled the fire until it blazed up. Sita pressed her hands together as if in prayer and walked round Rama three times to the right. Then, suddenly, she stepped fearlessly into the flames. But Agni, god of fire, led her through unharmed. Now Sita was even more beautiful. Then Rama spoke to the watching crowd. 'I never doubted Sita, but I wished to prove her love, before everyone.' And, smiling, he took her in his arms. At last, they were together again.

Then Rama with Sita close beside him, climbed on to Ravana's chariot. Lakshmana joined them. After Rama thanked all his friends and waved goodbye, the chariot soared across land and sea. Finally, the three travellers arrived home in Koshala to a great welcome, and Rama was acclaimed.

He reigned for many happy years. There was peace, justice and prosperity. So much so, that if people now speak of happiness or look forward to a better time, they say, 'May it be as in the reign of mighty Rama!'

Lone Bird – Shadow on the Moon

This legend was recorded in 1848 by archaeologist Ephraim Squier, who heard it by a campfire on the shore of Lake Superior related by a chief of the Chippewas. Each Indian tribe had its own local beliefs but they also had a number of beliefs in common. Many concentrate on explanations for the happenings of nature which so closely ruled their lives. Thus *Lone Bird* explains the origin of the 'face' in the full moon. It also teaches that whatever else happens in the world, nature goes on for ever.

Many snows ago, before the White Man came to take the Indian lands, people of the Chippewa tribe were great and strong. And they were as many as leaves upon the maple tree, their tents as countless as the stars in the sky. They hunted buffalo on the prairies of the West, trapped beaver in the rivers, caught deer in the forest around the Great Lakes and fished in the streams that flow from the mountains towards the rising sun.

They were feared and respected by their enemies and loved by all their friends. The Good Spirit, chief of life, was pleased with his children. And his children were content.

In those long-ago years, on the shores of the big water, now Lake Superior, lived an Indian maid called Lone Bird. She was the only child of her mother, She Eagle, and her father, Dawn of Day. Lone Bird was as graceful as a silver birch, her voice like the river's song at twilight; no daughter of the tribe had such proud, fine looks.

From all the camps of the Chippewa nation young braves came to seek Lone Bird to be their wife. But she stared coolly at them all, unmoved as they sang of their skill at hunting and daring in war. In vain they brought gifts to the lodge of She Eagle and Dawn of Day but the heart of the maid was, they thought, like winter ice and each brave returned home dismayed.

Dawn of Day, anxious at his daughter's coolness, praised the skill and courage of the braves he knew. He told her that no maid in the tribe had so noble a band of suitors from whom to choose. But when her father had spoken, Lone Bird took his hand and, smiling, said, 'Do I not have my mother's love and my father to protect me? What need have I to wed?'

Dawn of Day made no reply for he did not understand. Next day, he left his lodge, summoned the unmarried braves of the camp and told them of his plan. 'All who wish to marry my daughter should gather on the shore of the lake. A race will be run. He who is fastest shall take my daughter as his prize, and lead her to his lodge.' So the young men eagerly prepared for the race, each hoping for the deer's swiftness of foot.

News of the contest spread throughout the camps of the Chippewa tribe, and braves came from far and near. On the morning of the race, a great crowd gathered. The elders were there as judges. Mothers were there to comfort their sons and to look for any other suitable brides. Fathers came seeking worthy husbands for their daughters. The daughters, in turn, hoped to be noticed by the braves who were painted in the finest colours and plumed with eagle and turkey cock feathers. Only one member of the tribe was missing–Lone Bird. She sat, sobbing in her parents' lodge. When everything was ready for the contest, the bronze-muscled braves lined up, their hearts beating like war drums. On a signal, they all dashed forward in a jostling crowd.

Soon two runners had broken free from the others. They were Bending Bow and Hunter of Deer. Both had loved Lone Bird for many moons. Each was fleet-footed, as swift as the rushing wind. And when both runners reached the finishing line, the judges could not tell who had won. So Bending Bow and Hunter of Deer raced again, and once more they came in side by side. A third time they ran, and no winner could be declared.

Lone Bird gazed longingly at the bright moon. Stretching up her arms, she cried, 'Oh, how beautiful you are.'

'Let them jump against each other,' someone said. Yet when they did, neither could beat the other by even a hair. The Good Spirit was acting here.

As Dawn of Day returned to his lodge with troubled mind, he found his daughter there, her head bowed and eyes red from weeping. Dawn of Day dearly loved his only child. Lifting her head, he spoke gently to her, 'You must not weep, my daughter. Everyone must marry.'

'But why do you wish to cast me from you?' she replied. 'Is your lodge not large enough for me, too?' Dawn of Day decided at once. 'You are right, Lone Bird. You shall never leave your parents' lodge against your will.'

Quickly, he returned to the elders still gathered beside the lake. 'The contest is over,' he announced. 'Bending Bow and Hunter of Deer have done well, but it is clearly the Good Spirit's will that my daughter shall remain unmarried.' And so the braves sadly returned to their camps.

Summer passed, leaves fell, the cold winds of winter blew across the lake. Then, in spring, the snows began to melt. The sun was warm, the air full of the smell of fir and pine, yet Lone Bird felt sad. She thought of her parents, of their white hair and faltering steps. She knew that their journey to the spirits was not far off.

'What will become of me when they are gone?' she thought. 'I have no children of my own, or company to brighten my passing days.' And for the first time in her life, she felt the fear of loneliness. As she gazed down the slope at the first flowers, she saw that they grew in pairs, two on each stem. Then she watched birds flying and busily building nests. They too lived in pairs.

'No flowers, or birds, or even wild geese live alone,' she murmured. 'It is not meant to be. But I am still glad I did not marry,' she sighed.

For a long time she sat above the lake, wrapped in her lonely thoughts. When she rose to leave, it was already dusk and the full moon cast a silver path across the lake. Lone Bird gazed longingly at the bright moon. Stretching up her arms, she cried, 'Oh, how beautiful you are. If only I had you to love, I would not feel lonely.' The Good Spirit was listening and his heart was moved. And on unseen hands, Lone Bird was lifted up to the moon.

When Dawn of Day had finished his work upon the slopes, he looked for his daughter. When he did not find her in the lodge, he returned to Maple Syrup Hill. From there he called her name, time and time again. But no answer came. His anxious gaze searched the trees, the slopes, the surface of the lake. Then, in desperation, he went to call to the Good Spirit, and looked up to the sky towards the shining moon. Could it be? Yes; he clearly saw his daughter smiling down, held in the moon's pale arms. Lone Bird seemed to say she was at peace. No longer did Dawn of Day or She Eagle worry about their daughter. They knew that Lone Bird would be cared for by the loving moon.

Many, many snows have passed since the days of Lone Bird and her Chippewa tribe. Their people have become weak and few, their tents are scattered to the winds. White strangers occupy their hunting grounds and the graves of their dead go unmourned. But flowers still bloom in spring, birds still build their nests, and the stars still shine. And if you look up to the moon, you can still see the face of Lone Bird smiling down. She gives hope to her people as they tell her story by the fading light of their lodge fires.

A Story of the Kikuyu

Kenya, a large country in East Africa, was named after a great volcano with three high peaks. Today it is known as Mount Kenya, but the Kikuyu, the country's largest tribe, call it Kere Nyaga. Kere Nyaga means 'Mountain of Brightness' or 'Whiteness' or 'Mystery', and the Kikuyu believe that it was made by God as a home for Himself on earth.

According to Kikuyu myth it was from Kere Nyaga that God created three great tribes of Kenya–the Kikuyu themselves, the Masai and the Chamba. As the story reveals, however, the founder of the Kikuyu tribe needed God's help more than once in order to establish his people.

One day, God called his three sons to him and showed them three objects. The first was a spear, the second a bow and the last a digging-stick. God told his sons to choose which one they wanted, and this would decide the sort of life they were going to lead. The choice was very important, for each of the three was going to be the father of a tribe of Kenya, and the choice would determine their way of life, too. Kamba, afterwards father of the Chamba tribe, chose the bow. So, he was sent off into the forest to become a hunter and shoot birds and other animals. Masai, father of the Masai tribe, preferred the spear. So, God told him he must go to the great flat lands called the plains and there look after herds of cattle.

Kikuyu, like his brothers, considered the three objects carefully and finally decided to have the digging-stick. This was a stick for making holes in the earth so that seeds could be planted and crops could grow. In this way, Kikuyu became a farmer and later on, the Kikuyu tribe worked on the land to cultivate peas, beans, sweet potatoes and other crops.

For his farming, their ancester, Kikuyu, was given a beautiful stretch of country where a mass of fig-trees grew. God took Kikuyu up the slopes of Kere Nyaga and told him to look around him. Far below, stretched out as far as the horizon, were the splendid lands which God had made. There were massive forests and wide plains, mighty rivers, and all the different birds and animals which lived in them.

Kikuyu marvelled at this wonderful sight. Then, his attention was caught by the place, right in the middle of the country, where all the fig trees grew. This, said Kikuyu, was the land he wanted, and God gave it to him.

Kikuyu set off to travel to his new land. When he got there, he found it was a truly marvellous place. The fig trees were strong and full of fruit. The grass was fresh and sweet-smelling. There was also a surprise awaiting Kikuyu. God had sent a beautiful woman called Moombi, the 'Moulder' or 'Creator', to be his wife.

In time, Kikuyu and Moombi had nine children. All of them were girls. Kikuyu was very pleased with his daughters, but he wanted sons as well.

Kikuyu decided to return to Kere Nyaga and ask God to help him. Moombi and their nine daughters went with him.

God listened to what Kikuyu had to say and then told him: 'Your wish will be granted, if you will do as I tell you.'

Kikuyu, of course, followed God's instructions in every way. First, he took a lamb and a kid, or young goat, to where a large fig tree stood. There, Kikuyu sacrificed the two animals and poured their blood and fat over the trunk of the tree. Next, Kikuyu called on Moombi and the nine daughters to make a burnt offering to God. The offering consisted of the animal's flesh.

Afterwards, Kikuyu and his wife and family went home to the place where the fig-trees grew. When they reached it, they were amazed and delighted to find nine young men waiting for them.

Kikuyu welcomed the young men with great joy and a big feast was held in their honour. A ram was killed to provide meat for the banquet, and a large quantity of millet was prepared and cooked. It was a great and happy occasion and everyone enjoyed themselves.

Kikuyu set off to travel
to his new land. When he
got there, he found it
was a truly marvellous
place. The fig trees were
strong and full of fruit.

Next day, Kikuyu took the nine young men aside and suggested that each marry one of his daughters. However, Kikuyu made an important condition.

'I do not want my daughters to go away from home,' he told the young men. 'After you marry them, you must stay here and live with my wife and myself. And when you have children, your families must bear the names of their mothers. The whole family will be called the family of Moombi, after my wife. Do you agree?'

The nine young men all nodded. So, nine weddings took place and after many years, the nine new families or tribes grew very numerous.

Kikuyu and Moombi grew old and died, and after their death, their land and possessions were divided up between their nine daughters. More time passed and the family of Moombi grew so large that the place of the fig-trees could not provide enough room for everyone.

So, the nine daughters of Moombi and Kikuyu each founded a separate clan or group, each of which bore her own name. This is what their father Kikuyu had wanted. The nine clans became the chief clans of the Kikuyu tribe and the whole group was still known as the tribe of Moombi.

In the tribe of Moombi, the women were, of course, more important than the men. Each woman had several husbands and when their husbands displeased them, they punished them severely.

After a while, the men grew tired of this harsh treatment and decided to rebel against the women. The problem was, though, that the women were very strong and fierce and very good fighters.

So the men decided to wait for a time until the chance came for their planned revolt to be successful. After a few months, it became clear that the women were all expecting babies. This meant they were very occupied and did not have their full strength. And this was the moment the men chose to rebel.

Very quickly, the men replaced the women as chiefs of the clans. They renamed the whole group after Kikuyu, their original father. Instead of each woman having several husbands, the men made a law that each of them should have several wives. And instead of each clan being named after a woman, the rebels gave each a man's name instead.

The Kikuyu men, in other words, tried to change everything so that they, and not the women, would be the more important. The women, however, refused to accept these changes. They wanted things to be as they were before. To get their way, the women used a frightful threat.

'Whenever we give birth to boys,' they threatened. 'We will at once kill them. Only our girl children will be permitted to live.' What was more, the women promised, they would refuse to have any more children after that. The men, of course, were horrified at this.

'We will have to give in,' they said. 'If the women do as they have threatened, it will mean the end of the whole tribe!'

So, the men yielded and the women once more became the strong and dominant members of the tribe. This is why, today, the Kikuyu clans of Kenya are still known by the names of the nine daughters of Kikuyu and Moombi, although the whole tribe bears Kikuyu's name.

The Willow Pattern Plate

The tale of the Willow Pattern Plate is a story of Ancient China. However, its origins are neither Chinese, nor ancient. The Willow Pattern was devised about two centuries ago as a design on crockery by the English craftsman, Thomas Minton.

In the 19th century, Willow Pattern china became extremely popular and a story grew up, using the features of the pattern—the Chinese pagodas, the quaint bridge, a pair of bluebirds and, of course, the weeping willow tree. It is a love story, about a mandarin's daughter and a poor shepherd boy who fall in love. They are parted by her angry father, but the lovers are reunited and escape with the help of a Chinese goddess.

T'so Ling the mandarin had everything a man could wish for. The mandarins who lived in China long ago were rich and powerful landowners and T'so Ling possessed vast lands and beautiful palaces. He wore clothes made of the finest silk and brocade and decorated with priceless jewels. He ate the finest food from plates made of gold and silver. Thousands of servants and labourers worked for T'so Ling.

No wonder T'so Ling was proud and haughty and considered himself a great man. He also thought himself extremely fortunate, not only because of his huge wealth but because he had a very beautiful daughter called Koong-se. T'so Ling loved Koong-se more than anything else in the world. She had a skin like soft satin and lovely long black hair and she was very graceful and gentle.

T'so Ling thought of his daughter as his most splendid treasure and he would do anything he could to please her and make her happy. Koong-se loved natural things–the sunshine dancing and sparkling on the waters of the river, the lovely green trees of summertime and the birds singing.

A river flowed through T'so Ling's land close to his palace. In the middle of the river there was a small island and just opposite on the river bank, there grew a willow tree. T'so Ling decided to build a summerhouse on the island, just for Koong-se. It was a delightful little building, beautifully decorated and furnished. T'so Ling also built a small curving bridge across to the island so that Koong-se could walk over to the summerhouse from the river bank.

Koong-se loved the summerhouse. Every day she went there, accompanied by her nurse. 'It is so lovely here,' Koong-se thought happily. 'I wish someone would write a poem about it.'

Koong-se was very fond of poetry. She loved beautiful words as much as she loved the beautiful scenes of nature. Her nurse used to read poems to her as she sat in the summerhouse, but they were not about the river or the birds.

Then, one day, Koong-se met a poet. She did not know he was a poet, for he worked for her father as a shepherd. His name was Chang and when he wrote poetry, he did it in secret. Chang was only a humble peasant boy and in ancient China, peasants were not able to write at all let alone write poetry.

While Chang was watching T'so Ling's sheep, he saw Koong-se and her nurse crossing the bridge to the little summerhouse. Chang thought Koong-se was the loveliest girl he had ever seen and he fell in love with her instantly. Koong-se soon noticed the handsome young man who always seemed to be waiting and watching out for her, and before long, she had fallen in love with Chang and wanted to meet him.

She sent a message to the shepherd asking him to visit her in the summerhouse. When Chang and Koong-se saw each other close to for the first time, they fell even more deeply in love than before.

After that, Chang came to the little summerhouse almost every day. Of course, Koong-se and the nurse realised that if T'so Ling found out, he would be very angry. A shepherd boy was far too humble and lowly even to speak to a mandarin's daughter. So, when Chang came, the old nurse kept watch.

While she watched, Koong-se and Chang talked together and admired the river and the willow tree and sometimes, Chang read his poems out loud. Koong-se and Chang were very happy until one day, the nurse fell asleep.

Koong-se burst into tears and begged her father to forgive Chang. 'Please, please do not send him away! I could not bear it!'

Unfortunately, that very day, T'so Ling decided to visit his daughter. The nurse, of course, did not notice T'so Ling approach across the bridge and when he found Koong-se and Chang together, he was furious.

'How dare you come here and speak to my daughter!' he shouted at Chang. 'Get out of here at once . . . and get out of my lands for ever.

At this, Koong-se burst into tears and begged her father to forgive Chang. 'Please, please do not send him away! I could not bear it!' Koong-se wept.

But T'so Ling would not listen. He looked angrily at his daughter. 'Think yourself lucky I have not ordered Chang to be executed!' was all he could say.

So, Chang went away with a heavy heart, thinking he would never see his beautiful Koong-se again. The nurse, too, was told to leave and now Koong-se was left all alone.

T'so Ling feared that Chang might try to come back. To prevent this, he built a pavilion close to his palace. The windows were made of black glass so that no one could see in. It was like a prison. T'so Ling ordered Koong-se to stay inside the pavilion and refused to allow her to leave it. So, poor Koong-se had not only lost Chang but the lovely sights and sounds of nature she enjoyed so much before. She spent her days in the dark pavilion, weeping and lamenting over her misfortune.

Meanwhile, T'so Ling, still afraid that Chang would return, had a huge, high fence built around his land to keep the shepherd boy out. He also decided that his daughter must marry a rich mandarin who owned lands nearby. This marriage, T'so Ling believed, would keep Koong-se and Chang apart for ever.

Koong-se was horrified. She hated the mandarin her father had chosen for her, for although very rich he was a cruel man and a bully.

Koong-se began to feel desperate. But, there was one way she might be able

88

to prevent her marriage to the mandarin. From time to time, a fishing boat came close to the pavilion where she was imprisoned. The next time it appeared on the river, Koong-se managed to attract the attention of the fisherman.

'Find Chang the shepherd boy,' Koong-se begged him. 'Tell him I am being forced to marry against my will. Chang must rescue me, or I am lost. . . .'

The fisherman felt very sorry for the beautiful Koong-se and agreed to take her message to Chang. Koong-se knew that what she had asked was very dangerous for the fisherman. Her father's guards might catch him and he would be severely punished. So, she prayed to the goddess Kwan-yin to keep the fisherman safe until he could find Chang and deliver the message.

Time passed. Spring came round again and the cherry trees blossomed. Koong-se's wedding day came closer and closer. But still there was no word from Chang. Perhaps the fisherman had been caught after all and Chang did not know of her plight.

Then, the wedding day dawned. There were great festivities and banquets were held in T'so Ling's palace and T'so Ling made a great fuss of his new son-in-law, the cruel mandarin. Everyone was happy, except for Koong-se, who alone in the dark pavilion, wept without ceasing. She had now begun to believe that Chang was dead and that there was no hope of escape for her. But Koong-se was wrong.

The fisherman had managed to reach Chang, guided by the goddess Kwan-yin. Chang knew all about the high fence T'so Ling had erected around his lands and realised that the only way to get in was to disguise himself as a wedding guest. So, the shepherd boy entered the palace and waited until the feasting was at its height.

Then, while T'so Ling and his guests were busy celebrating and enjoying themselves, Chang slipped out of the palace and into the pavilion next door. As soon as she saw him, Koong-se's tears changed to joy and she flung her arms around Chang's neck and kissed him over and over again.

'We must be quick,' Chang whispered urgently. 'It will not be easy.'

Koong-se agreed. She waited only to roll her possessions into a mat and then, with Chang, she ran out of the pavilion. They took shelter in the little summerhouse where they had once been so happy together. There, Chang said, the fisherman was waiting to take them away by boat. But Chang's plan had already gone wrong. One of T'so Ling's guards had seen Chang and Koong-se as they crossed the bridge to the summerhouse. He made a great outcry, shouting loudly and cracking his whip.

Their plight was desperate. They could not reach the fishing boat and they could not run away. 'Kwan-yin will help us!' Koong-se told Chang.

Koong-se prayed hard to the goddess, begging her to come to the rescue. Kwan-yin heard her prayers and acted quickly. All at once, Koong-se and Chang found themselves turned into bluebirds. Together, they spread their wings and flew high up into the sky.

Before long, Koong-se and Chang were so high up that the palace looked no bigger than a box and the river by it was a narrow ribbon shining in the sunlight. They flew away, towards the horizon, free and together at last.

The Death of Roland

One summer's day in the year 778, as the Emperor Charlemagne was leading his army home to France from Spain he was attacked in the Pyrenees by a party of Basques. He lost his rearguard at the Roncevaux Pass. Nearly three hundred years later a poet wrote the story down, calling it *The Song of Roland*; by then no one remembered the facts of the battle, so it became legend not history. At the time the tale was written, the crusades to the Holy Land were beginning and Roland, the fearless young Christian knight, was the kind of hero Christians wished to believe in, whether he had existed or not. And instead of Basques the author changed the enemy to Saracens.

So the tale is true in spirit if not in every detail.

For seven years the mighty French Emperor, Charlemagne, had been fighting the Saracens in Spain, but at last the long campaign was nearly over. The only city walls left for him to topple were those of Saragossa in the north of Spain. As the Emperor was preparing for his march on Saragossa, messengers arrived from the Saracen king of the city, Marsile.

Charlemagne and his men were resting in an orchard outside Cordova. Among them was the Emperor's nephew Roland, a bold and daring knight who had won many victories for Charlemagne. The horn that he carried at his side had sounded on battlefields all over Spain and struck fear into the hearts of many a Saracen foe. In the shade of a pine tree sat the aged Charlemagne upon a golden throne.

When the messengers arrived upon their snow-white mules, bearing olive branches in their right hands, they bowed before the Emperor and delivered their terms: 'May your god preserve you, Charlemagne. Our lord, Marsile, begs you to return to France; you have stayed too long in Spain. Marsile will come to you there and offer his allegiance to you.'

The Emperor bowed his head in thought, then looked up frowning. 'But how can I believe your lord's word?'

'He will give you twenty hostages, our most noble young men, even his own son. If we betray our word, we know you will kill these men.'

The Saracens were so desperate, they were ready to sacrifice their best sons to save their town and rid Spain of Charlemagne.

While the messengers slept the night under the Emperor's care, he called a council of his barons to discuss King Marsile's terms.

Amidst the murmurs and uncertain shakes of head, bold Roland sprang to his feet to speak. 'It is seven years since we came to Spain. We have waged war

Among them was the Emperor's nephew Roland, a bold and daring knight.

The Emperor sat with head bowed low, clasping his chin and tugging at his beard. He was tired of war and so were many of his men.

and won. So let us go on to this final battle; when we take Saragossa we will have all of Spain.'

There was silence.

The Emperor sat with head bowed low, clasping his chin and tugging at his beard. He was tired of war. So were many of his men. At last Ganelon, Roland's godfather, stood up. He was bitterly jealous of the young man's glory. 'Since King Marsile sends word that he'll swear allegiance, Spain is already conquered. Spiteful pride is wrong; we've fought enough.'

Others had their say and at last it was decided to send a man to Saragossa to seal the pact. But who? It might be a trap and the envoy could be slain.

'I'll go,' cried Roland.

But his friend, Oliver, pulled him back, fearing his hasty temper. 'You're too headstrong' he said.

'Then, if you won't send me,' said Roland, 'send my godfather Ganelon.'

At once the French agreed but Ganelon took it as an insult. Flinging down his cloak, he strode forward, his eyes sparkling angrily. 'So, Roland, you now tell me what I'm to do. If I return, I'll make you suffer for this insult.'

'You are too proud,' said Roland. 'Everyone knows I meant no harm. But if the Emperor agrees I am quite prepared to go.'

'You will not go for my sake,' cried Ganelon in a rage. And striding proudly to the Emperor he took the royal glove, a token of his mission.

Ganelon rode off to the Saracen king, burning to have his revenge on Roland, and on the way he hatched a wicked plot. When he came before King Marsile, he told him 'There is only one knight who urges war upon you. His foolish pride will be his downfall, and yours if you let him live. Once Charlemagne is in France, he will not bother to return if Roland is not there to urge him.'

Then the treacherous Ganelon told Marsile his plan. 'Charlemagne has to cross the Pyrenees by the pass of Roncevaux. He'll set a guard behind him: Roland and twenty thousand Franks. Now, if you lead eighty thousand Saracens against this rearguard and trap them in the pass, you can kill them all and be free of Roland for good. You will never know war again. The loss of Roland's life will be like tearing the right arm from Charlemagne.'

The Saracen king was generous in reward, then they kissed to seal the deed.

Off rode Ganelon, leading a train of tribute for the Emperor: silver and gold on seven hundred camels, and twenty noble young men as hostages. And, in his pouch, he had the keys to Saragossa.

At dawn, just as it grew light, Ganelon rode into camp. 'God keep you, Sire,' he told Charlemagne. 'I bear you the keys to Saragossa, a handsome tribute and twenty men as hostages. The infidel king vows he will follow you to France within a month.'

The Emperor was delighted. Straightaway he bade a thousand trumpets sound: To France! To France! Swords were strapped to sides, helmets laced, lances sharpened; and off they rode homewards. Day and night passed, and by now the army was wending its way through the Pyrenees. All of a sudden, the Emperor halted. 'My lord barons,' he cried. 'Who will guard our rear?'

'There is my godson, Roland,' called Ganelon. 'No one has more courage.'

Roland, of course, agreed. He took twenty thousand men including his comrade Oliver and the lords Gerins and Geriers.

The peaks were high, the valleys shaded, and the narrow passes were full of danger. Roland took his stand in the Spanish Pass at Roncevaux, giving the main body of the army time to march away safely. As the twenty thousand men settled down to wait, good Oliver climbed a high peak to spy out the green valley beyond. He gasped as he saw the approaching Saracens, so many he could not count their ranks, helmets gleaming in the sun, shields glittering, swords and spears all fixed. His heart raced with fear. As fast as he could, he came down from the peak to warn the others. 'Roland, quick, sound your horn to summon back Charlemagne. We are outnumbered by the Saracens, twenty to one.'

'Never, by God,' cried Roland. 'My glory would turn to shame. With my blade, Durandal, I'll slay the pagan horde myself.'

Twice more Oliver begged him to sound his horn, but he pleaded in vain. Roland had pride; Oliver had wisdom, but both had courage. They would rather die than leave the pass. So the rearguard prepared for the coming fight. Then brave Roland spoke up, rallying his men. 'Lords and barons, hold your ground; give as good as you get. Your deeds will live forever.'

Great shouts of 'Hurrah!' rolled through the pass.

By now the Saracens were almost upon the French. They could clearly hear the words of the Saracen chief: 'You are betrayed by your own king. He has left you here to die while he escapes.'

When Roland heard that, he was so enraged, he spurred on his steed and struck the man full force with his spear, breaking his shield and piercing his heart.

Next Oliver, pricked his horse with golden spurs and ran through a pagan duke, flinging him dead into the dust. Soon all the men were engaged in combat. Roland struck about him so fiercely with his spear that fifteen men lay dead and his shaft was broken in two. He therefore bared his good sword Durandal and continued through the pass, waving the blood-stained sword. The Saracen bodies lay in heaps, the green grass running with their blood. So many young men of both sides lay dead, never to see their wives or mothers again. The Saracens were slain by the thousand, so that not two thousand remained.

Yet just as the battle seemed won, the Saracen King, Marsile, appeared, riding through the valley with another twenty columns of men. Yet the French still fought on, so fiercely that the Saracens had to withdraw. That gave the French a brief respite. Roland counted his men: only sixty left.

'I'll sound my horn,' Roland said to Oliver. 'If Charlemagne hears, he'll turn about and come to our aid.'

'It is too late,' said Oliver. 'You should have blown it when I begged. If the Emperor had come then we would not have suffered so much loss. But blow it anyway so that the Emperor will come and take revenge.'

So Roland put the horn to his lips and blew with all his might. It rang out loud and clear and in the far distance Charlemagne heard it.

'Roland needs help,' he cried.

'Roland is too bold to need our aid,' said Ganelon in the Emperor's ear. 'It is the whistle of the wind about these peaks.'

Hearing no answering call, Roland blew even harder on his horn.

'I do hear Roland's horn,' cried Charlemagne.

'He does not need our help; that would bring him shame,' said Ganelon. 'Let's leave him be.'

In grief and pain, Roland sounded his horn a third time, a vein bursting in his temples at the strain.

'Roland blows in pain,' the Emperor cried. 'There is battle for sure. Wheel about and go to his aid.'

On his order, trumpets blew an answering call, and his army rode to Roland's aid. Charlemagne now realized he had been tricked by the traitor Ganelon so he had him clapped in irons.

But the peaks were high, shadowy and grand. The valleys were deep and the rivers ran swiftly. It would take the Emperor's army precious time to reach the trapped men. They had held back too long.

Roland meanwhile gazed at the barren mountains, then at the dead men lying all about and a great rage surged through him. Wielding Durandal, he flew at the Saracens, scattering them to the wind. 'Strike on,' he shouted, rallying his men. 'Give the foe no quarter!'

All knew it was a fight to the death. King Marsile came riding into the fray, slaying several bold dukes. As Roland saw him, he cried, 'You'll pay for slaying my companions. When Charlemagne arrives he'll see fifteen enemy dead for every one of ours.' Thereupon he rushed forward and sliced off the king's right hand. The king turned and fled, and as he did so, Roland struck off the head of his son, Jursalu, before he could escape. He put many Saracens to flight, leaving only the hardiest men in Spain. One struck Oliver from behind, breaking his backbone. Yet feeling death approaching fast, he struck the man hard upon the head and killed him. Then, calling to Roland, he gasped, 'My friend, bitter grief must part us now.'

As Roland looked upon Oliver's pale face, he saw his friend was dead. Nowhere on earth was there a more heartbroken man than Roland at that moment.

Now only three were left: Roland, Archbishop Turpin and Lord Gualtier. And the three stood abreast at the entry to the pass. Roland engaged twenty men, Gualtier six and Turpin five. The line held firm. But another forty thousand men were coming through the valley. Not daring to engage the dauntless trio, they stood back and hurled lances and spears, arrows, barbs, darts and javelins. Under the first flight, brave Gualtier fell, and Turpin was badly wounded. But Roland was unharmed. Brave Archbishop Turpin rose from his fallen horse and staggered to stand at Roland's side. Roland was in great pain: his head ached from the broken temple vein. Yet now he sounded his horn again, just loud enough to reach the Emperor.

'My lords,' sighed the Emperor. 'This day Roland will be dead. I hear his horn blown with scarcely any breath. Faster, faster! Sound your horns for the Saracens to hear.'

The sixty thousand trumpets blared out, ringing through the valleys. The Saracens knew they had to slay Roland swiftly and flee. Four hundred men made one last attack on him. He sat there proudly on his horse, guarding the pass and letting no man by. The wounded Archbishop stood unsteadily beside Roland's horse.

Another shower of spears came down, this time killing Roland's horse and pinning the brave Archbishop to the ground. Yet still nothing touched brave Roland. He stood up from his fallen horse and ran to aid his friend, laying him gently on the grass. With his dying breath Archbishop Turpin said, 'Return to the fight. The field is yours. God be with you, Roland!'

Roland stood alone. Soon he felt the cold breath of death upon his cheek, but with sword in one hand, horn in the other, he climbed to a high rock to defy the foe. Alas, the effort was too great and he fell senseless to the ground.

Now Roland felt death creeping through his body. He lay upon the grass, placing his horn and sword beneath his body, and turning his head towards the foe. The Emperor would know he had died facing the enemy hordes. At the moment Charlemagne entered the pass, brave Roland breathed his last.

There was no path or passage anywhere in the valley of Roncevaux, for bodies of French and Saracens covered every foot of ground. When Charlemagne saw his lords lying dead–his nephew Roland, his brave Archbishop, Counts Oliver, Gerins and Sansum, he tore his beard in grief and fell upon his knees.

Roland climbed to a high
rock to defy the foe.
Alas, the effort was too
great and he fell to the
ground. Now Roland felt
death creeping through
his body.

But a cry from the Duke of Nîmes disturbed his weeping. 'Look, Sire, less than a league away, dust is rising. It is the treacherous Saracens. Let us ride quickly and take revenge.'

Through the valley rode the French, chasing the Saracens towards Saragossa, killing stragglers as they went. They barred every sideroad until the enemy army reached the high bank of the River Sebre. There was no way forward or back but at a command, they all leapt into the deep, swirling river. Many sank to the bottom straightaway weighed down by their armour; others were swept downstream and out to sea. Few escaped the watery grave.

The tale of vengeance is swiftly told. King Marsile was slain, and his city was taken. Ganelon the traitor was put to death.

When the Emperor was revenged, his great rage died. But it was not long before he too sank into the dark sleep of death.

But legend has it that if the French ever need his aid, he will heed the call, rise up, and summon brave Roland and his men. And they will ride into battle together once again.

William Tell

No one knows whether William Tell, the national hero of Switzerland, was a real person or not. However, there are many stories about his exploits and his bravery and skill in fighting the Austrians who dominated Switzerland seven centuries ago. Tell's story was first written down in a ballad some time before 1474, and the tale was retold several times after that.

The popular story of William Tell which we know today deals with the enmity between him, and the cruel Austrian governor Gessler. Gessler tries to trick Tell into killing his son by shooting an apple off the top of the boy's head. Afterwards, Tell is taken prisoner but escapes and not only gets his revenge on Gessler, but helps to set Switzerland free.

illiam Tell was a man who loved his freedom. He was happiest when he could go up into the mountains and breathe in their pure, icy air and look down from high ledges at the lovely silvery lakes and the fringe of pine trees around their shores. Beyond the lakes were more mountains, cloaked in snow, and Tell could spend long hours up there alone with the little wild goats called chamois which he hunted for food.

Tell was as much at home in the mountains as the chamois or the flocks of sheep which grazed on their slopes. Like them, he could leap across narrow ravines, or climb steep rocks and make his way across icy glaciers without slipping. Sometimes, Tell was away from his home for days at a time, with only the mountain creatures and the icy, snowy landscape for company.

Tell knew though, how precious his own freedom was, for his country, Switzerland, was not free. It was ruled by the Austrians who were cruel and greedy tyrants. The cruellest and greediest of all was the Austrian governor, Gessler, who was hated throughout the land for his wicked deeds. If a Swiss farmer refused to pay a fine, Gessler took his lands fom him. When Gessler wanted to have a feast at his castle, he ordered a shepherd to hand over his entire flock of sheep so that they could be killed for meat. If someone failed to salute him as he rode past, that man was sent into exile.

As Governor of Switzerland, Gessler was only the representative of the Austrian Emperor. However, Gessler often behaved as if he were the Emperor himself.

One day, Gessler commanded that his fur-trimmed cap should be placed on a pike and the pike stuck in the ground at the centre of the town. Everyone who passed by was ordered to take off their hats and kneel before the cap as a mark of respect.

Gessler commanded that his fur-trimmed cap should be placed on a pike and the pike stuck in the ground at the centre of the town.

99

Some of the townsfolk treated the order as a joke. Others threw rocks at the governor's cap, then ran away before the Austrian guards could catch them. Others avoided the town centre, so that they would not have to pass by the cap and salute it.

William Tell hardly ever went into the town because he spent most of his time in the mountains. So, he did not know about the governor's orders. Unfortunately, on the very day the pike was set up, Tell took his young son Walter into town to see his grandfather.

As Tell and his son walked through the town centre, they were surprised to see it so deserted, and did not notice the pike with the cap on top of it. So, they walked on, heading for the grandfather's house.

Suddenly a voice shouted out: 'Hey, you there! Stop!' and, turning, William Tell saw to his surprise an Austrian guard running towards him. The guard looked menacing.

'Pay your respects to the governor's cap!' he demanded.

William Tell shrugged his shoulders and began to walk away. The guard came after him. 'Kneel before the governor's cap!' he insisted. 'And take your hat off–peasant!'

William Tell, thinking the whole thing was ridiculous, just ignored him. Suddenly, a second guard rushed up, seized hold of Tell and bound his hands behind his back. The first guard tried to grasp young Walter, but the boy managed to get away and ran off, shouting for help.

At once, a crowd of townspeople came rushing into the square and the two Austrians were surrounded.

Walter Furst, Tell's father-in-law, tried to reason with the two guards and offered them money if they would let Tell and young Walter go. One of the guards began to insist that Tell had broken the law and must be punished, but changed his mind when he saw that some people in the crowd had hatchets and knives in their hands.

He was just about to untie William Tell when a clatter of horses' hooves sounded in the square. It was Governor Gessler, dressed in a fur-trimmed red hunting tunic, and accompanied by a troop of horsemen. The horsemen pushed the crowd back and Gessler confronted Tell.

'So, we have caught you at last, William Tell,' Gessler sneered after the two guards had told him what had occurred. 'You have been plotting against our rule in Switzerland and against our Emperor. You shall die for it!'

Gessler's accusation was only partly true. William Tell was known as a loyal patriot and had certainly been involved in some of the plans made by farmers and others to overthrow Austrian rule in their country. He had also helped a farmer escape from his Austrian pursuers by ferrying him to safety across a stormy lake. But . . .

'I have never plotted against the Emperor,' Tell said firmly, looking Gessler straight in the eye. 'And I did not know of your order to salute your cap.'

Gessler, who hated William Tell, decided to play a game with him. As everyone knew, Tell was an expert at shooting with the crossbow which he used on his hunting expeditions into the mountains.

'Take your crossbow and shoot an apple which will be placed on your son's

William Tell took two
arrows from the quiver
on his back, put one in
his belt and fitted the
other into his crossbow.
Slowly and carefully, he
took aim.

head,' Gessler commanded. 'The distance will be one hundred paces. If you succeed, I will give you your life: if you fail, you will die!'

William Tell was horrified. If he missed the apple, he would have killed his beloved son. He began to beg Gessler to change his mind, but young Walter interrupted him.

'You are the greatest marksman in the whole world, father,' he said confidently. 'I will come to no harm.'

With that, young Walter went over to an apple tree, picked an apple and placed it on his head, then turned to face his father.

William Tell took two arrows from the quiver on his back, put one in his belt and fitted the other into his crossbow. Slowly and carefully, he took aim. As he let go of the bowstring, the arrow sped towards Walter. It struck the apple, neatly slicing it in two.

A huge cheer went up from the crowd and even Governor Gessler had to admire Tell's great skill.

'Well done!' he congratulated Tell. 'You have saved your own life. But tell me, why did you put a second arrow in your belt?'

'It was for you, Gessler,' Tell replied grimly. 'If I had missed and killed my son, I would have shot you dead where you stand now.'

Gessler's face turned red with fury. 'I gave you your life,' he growled at Tell. 'But for your wicked admittance, you shall spend it in the deepest dungeon in my castle!'

Gessler's soldiers surrounded William Tell and bound him in chains from head to foot. Then, they dragged him down to the shores of Lake Lucerne, where the governor's ship lay at anchor. There, they tied William Tell to the mast.

Gessler's castle lay on the other side of the lake and when the governor and his guards were safely on board, the ship headed out across the water. A strong wind was blowing and the surface of the lake was choppy. As the ship moved further and further out, the waves grew higher and higher, and an icy fog came down from the mountains.

The steersman was having great difficulty in holding the ship on a straight course. Before long, the vessel was being dragged towards the shore where the waves smashed down onto a line of rocks in showers of white spray. Soon, it seemed, the ship would strike the rocks and everyone on board would die. One of Gessler's soldiers remembered how William Tell had once steered a small boat safely across the lake in a violent storm, to help a farmer escape his pursuers. 'The prisoner can save us,' the soldier told Gessler. 'Give the order to untie him. Let him steer the ship to safety or we are all lost!'

Gessler was terrified at the danger that faced his ship, and was willing to do anything to save his own life. So, he ordered that William Tell be untied from the mast and promised him his freedom if he would save the ship.

Gessler, of course, had no intention of letting Tell go free: he wanted Tell to die in the dungeon he had promised him. William Tell, however, had a cunning plan of his own. Once he was freed from the mast, Tell made his way to the stern of the ship and grasped the tiller. Holding it tightly, Tell steered the ship towards the shore, where a large rock jutted out of the water. He

headed the ship directly towards it, then when it was only a metre or so away, swung the stern round so that it faced the rock.

Before anyone could stop him, William Tell snatched up his crossbow, which was lying close by, and leapt over the stern onto the rock. Pausing only to push the ship away, he began scrambling up the slippery wet surface until his hands grasped the grass at the top. He was safe.

Far below him, the governor's ship had been caught by a sudden change in the wind, which took it out into the middle of the lake. There, it disappeared from sight in the thick mist.

Just then, Tell felt the soft muzzle of a sheep against his back. He turned round and saw there was a whole flock of them. Their shepherd was standing nearby. Tell recognised him. It was old Kuoni, one of the members of the Rootli, a secret group of farmers who had sworn to overthrow the Austrians and drive them out of Switzerland. Their latest plan was to destroy the castles the Austrians had built.

Tell made his way to the stern of the ship and grasped the tiller. Holding it tightly, Tell steered the ship towards the shore, where a large rock jutted out of the water.

Kuoni greeted Tell with tears in his eyes. 'No man but you could have climbed the rock in such a storm and lived!' he said.

Tell smiled broadly. 'I have a great purpose to live for, my friend,' he replied. 'I must give the signal for the attack to begin on the Austrian castles! Was everything arranged when the Rootli met?' Kuoni nodded. 'Then tell everyone to watch for my signal. I will light a fire on the side of the rock of Mystenstein so that it can be seen all around the lake. Then the Austrians will see how fiercely we Swiss can fight for our freedom.'

Kuoni, however, looked worried. 'You must remain in hiding, friend Tell,' he warned. 'I saw Gessler's ship miss the rocks and drift out into the lake. Suppose the ship has survived the storm? If it has, then Gessler will soon be hunting for you.'

Kuoni was right. Gessler's ship *had* survived the storm and managed to reach safety. From a ridge high up the mountainside above Lake Lucerne, William Tell watched the governor and his soldiers stagger ashore, soaking wet from head to foot, and exhausted after their ordeal.

'A pity Gessler did not drown,' thought Tell. 'For now I must kill him myself. He deserves to die. He tried to make me murder my own son. His cruelty has brought great suffering to my people.' But despite his hatred for Gessler, William Tell disliked the idea of murdering him coldly and deliberately.

Reluctantly, he fitted an arrow in his crossbow and waited.

Far below, a horse had been brought for the governor and he climbed into the saddle. Then, just as he was about to ride off, a woman dashed out and threw herself on the ground in front of him. She was carrying two tiny babies.

'My husband has been in prison for six months!' she cried. 'My children are starving. I beg you, Governor, release him; he has committed no crime!'

Gessler was furious. 'Out of my way, woman!' he roared. 'Or my horses will run you down.'

The woman grasped hold of the reins on Gessler's horse and pleaded with him again. But he only repeated his threat.

'All right, then!' the woman screamed at him. 'Kill me and my children! We have nothing left to live for because of you!' With that, she flung herself down right in front of the horse's hooves. As Gessler kicked at his horse, ready to ride over her, William Tell, watching from high above, let loose his crossbow. The arrow sped down and struck Gessler in the heart. He toppled from the saddle and hit the ground with a thud. The hated governor was dead.

Pausing only to see that the woman and her babies were safe, Tell scrambled away across the mountainside. Gessler's soldiers searched, but could not find him. They were, in any case, afraid to follow Tell too far into the mountains in case he killed them, too.

Night fell over Lake Lucerne. Suddenly, a fire was seen blazing beside the rock of Mystenstein. Word spread through the villages around the lake that William Tell's signal had been seen, and the farmers gathered to carry out the plans made by the Rootli.

Before dawn, every Austrian castle had been attacked and the soldiers in the garrisons were all running for their lives. As a sign of their success, each group of rebels lit a beacon fire and as each fire was seen, another was lit until, right across Switzerland, fires were blazing out the news of the Austrians' defeat.

The rebels' met at the house of Tell's father-in-law, Walter Furst, and as they were all congratulating each other and drinking each other's health, a messenger burst in with marvellous news.

'The Emperor of Austria is dead!' he cried. 'His own nephew, Prince John, has killed him!'

The celebrations now reached even greater heights of joy, but the joy was not complete. William Tell was not there to share it.

'He has not been seen since he killed Gessler,' said Walter Furst. 'We must find him and tell him that Switzerland is free at last!'

William Tell, however, already knew. After he had lit the fire on Mystenstein, he had waited until he saw the beacons. Tell could not be sure that he would be safe if he left his hiding place in the mountains. So, he remained there and was still wandering along the high mountain trails when dawn came.

Just then, he saw a stranger stumbling towards him. It was a man, dressed like a monk in a long plain gown, and as he came close, Tell could see he was distressed and terrified.

'I thought you were an Austrian, hunting for me,' the man wept, shivering in the mountain cold. 'But you must be William Tell–even in Austria we have heard of your courage.'

The stranger was not a monk at all, but Prince John of Austria, who had fled into the mountains. 'I have done a terrible thing,' he confessed to William Tell, and then recounted how he had killed his uncle, the Emperor.

'I, too, have killed a man,' Tell confessed in his turn. 'Murder is a terrible thing, but evil men deserve to die. Between us, my friend,' he told Prince John, 'we have freed Switzerland from two cruel tyrants, and my people have their liberty at last.'

El Cid

No one knows who wrote the long narrative poem of the Cid, but we know it was written in about 1140. No doubt it had been recited in market places for some time before, even by those who remembered Rodrigo Diaz of Bivar, whom the Moors called El Cid–The Warrior. He was born about 1043 in a village to the north of Burgos in northern Spain at a time when the country was contested by warring Christians and Moors from North Africa. He died in Valencia at the age of 56 in 1099, having become a legend in his lifetime as a great commander.

Long ago, around 1043, when Spain was split between warring bands of Moors and Christians, Rodrigo Diaz was born in Bivar, a village to the north of the Castilian city of Burgos. His parents being of noble blood, he was brought up in the court of Prince Sancho, eldest son of King Fernando who at that time ruled Castile and Leon. The young Rodrigo Diaz soon showed himself to be a brave and daring warrior in the service of the Prince and was made a general. The Moors, in admiration, called the young general El Cid–the Warrior.

On the death of King Fernando, his sons at once started fighting for the kingdom, and it was not long before Prince Alfonso won. Sancho was killed and his famed general entered the service of Alfonso for whom he gained a great reputation and much wealth. King Alfonso was delighted and gave him permission to marry a lovely noblewoman, Dona Jimena. But there were those at court who were envious of El Cid and two lords constantly whispered evil to the king about him.

'He cannot be trusted,' they muttered. 'He will one day seek revenge for your brother's death.'

Eventually the king listened to their intrigues and banished El Cid from his realm.

In fact, El Cid was a man of honour and more loyal to Alfonso than any man. Exile grieved him greatly and he resolved to win back Alfonso's trust by daring deeds. Before he set off into exile, he called his wife and two daughters to him. 'I love you as I do my own soul but I must go from here and you must stay behind. Goodbye, my loved ones.'

That day 50 horsemen were ready to ride with him. He rode across the border of Castile, along the stone road of Quinea, crossing the River Duero at Navapalos, and paused for the night at the town of Figueruela. All that day men had gathered to join him. As he entered the Moorish kingdom of Toledo as many as three hundred lances, not counting foot soldiers, were assembled about him. At last they came to the town of Castejon on the bank of the River Henares.

All that night El Cid lay hidden. As dawn broke, the people of Castejon opened the gates and left the town to tend their fields. It was then, when few remained inside the walls, that El Cid emerged from hiding, rode through the gates, killing fifteen guards with his naked sword, and took the town with all its gold and silver treasure. Under his lieutenant, Minaya, a raiding party plundered all the land around, returning with their spoils: many flocks of sheep and cattle, horses and other wealth.

After receiving three hundred marks of silver from the Moors in ransom for his prisoners, El Cid proceeded to the lands of Saragossa held by the Moorish king of Valencia. There on a hillside outside Alcocer, he camped with his men, striking fear into the hearts of the Moors. But the city walls were strong and no gap could be found. El Cid remained there for 15 weeks and when he saw that Alcocer would not yield he thought up a plan.

Gathering up his tents he pretended to depart. The Moors rejoiced, crying, 'El Cid has no more food. Let us pursue and slay him!' And they gave chase, leaving the gates open with none to guard them. But El Cid wheeled about to

All that day, men had gathered to join him. As he entered the Moorish kingdom of Toledo, as many as three hundred lances, not counting foot soldiers, were assembled about him.

meet the enemy force, and his men attacked with such ferocity that they overran the Moors and charged on through the open gates into the town.

The townsmen sent a message to King Tamin of Valencia, telling him how the Cid had taken Alcocer and now threatened all the neighbouring towns.

'Take three thousand men,' the king told his generals, 'and bring back this warrior alive.'

Soon Alcocer was besieged by the enemy. At the end of three weeks, El Cid called a council. 'They have cut off our water,' he said. 'Our bread will soon be gone. If we leave by night they will stop us; if we let them attack us we shall be overwhelmed. We are only six hundred. We have no option but to attack them first: tomorrow at dawn.'

Next day, as the sun rose, El Cid rode out to meet his enemy. As many as a thousand Moors fell dead upon the field that day. El Cid himself accounted for thirty-four. His men sacked the Moors' encampment, seized arms and much wealth besides, and five hundred Arabian steeds. Among the Christians there was great joy, for only fifteen of their men were dead.

Great was the glory of El Cid from then on. Soon after, he laid siege to Valencia for nine full months, finally forcing the Moors to surrender. Then he entered the city as conqueror.

By now, three thousand six hundred men rode under El Cid's command and his wealth could not be counted. Now he was ready to show his loyalty to the king. Summoning his faithful comrade Minaya, he said, 'Go with two hundred horses, saddles and bridles to King Alfonso, kiss his hand and say I shall serve him as long as I live.'

The king was convinced. 'El Cid shall have my pardon, as he deserves. Let him come to me.'

When El Cid heard the news he made ready at once. He dressed magnificently in gold and red and took with him all his riches and spoils. On meeting the king he fell to his knees.

'Rise, rise, Cid,' the king cried out. 'With all my heart I pardon you and welcome you back to my realm.'

All who were there rejoiced at the sight. All but the two evil lords, Alvar Diaz and Garcia Ordonez. They too appeared to be celebrating the Cid's return and they urged the king to grant them, in marriage, El Cid's two daughters. He was most displeased, but would not offend the king by refusing.

'I give Dona Elvira and Dona Sol into your charge,' he told the king. 'Give them to whom you think best and I shall be content.'

For two full weeks the wedding feasts went on, and at the end, El Cid and his entourage, including the lords Diaz and Ordonez, departed for Valencia, where they lived together for two years. In that time El Cid repulsed yet another Moorish attack, but in the battle, his two sons-in-law turned tail and ran at the sound of the Moorish drums, fearing for their lives.

Many mocked them for their cowardice, and they resolved to return to their own lands in Carrion and avenge their honour. They took their wives with them. No sooner had they left the lands protected by El Cid, than the two evil men stopped in the glade of an oak wood and turned on their wives.

'Today you will suffer for our dishonour,' they cried. Thereupon they whipped the poor girls until their flesh was raw then left Dona Elvira and Dona Sol for dead in the oak wood.

But they did not die. Luckily, a shepherd, passing through the wood, heard the girls' moans. He tended them as best he could until one told him who they were. A message was quickly sent to El Cid, and the bold warrior grieved loud and long. 'I swear that these Carrion crows shall suffer for this.'

Without delay El Cid prepared a message, which was taken by his servant, to the king.

'The king gave my daughters in marriage. Let him now call a court to try the guilty men.'

On hearing the news the king was devastated. He gladly summoned a council of his counts and nobles. Both Alvar Diaz and Garcia Ordonez came with their followers, certain they were too strong and wealthy to be harmed.

They whipped the poor girls until their flesh was raw then left Dona Elvira and Dona Sol for dead in the oak wood. But they did not die.

When El Cid arrived, he was magnificently dressed in a woven shirt as white as the sun, a tunic of fine brocade and gold shoe buckles. His long beard was tied with a silken cord. All there were overawed by the handsome and imposing figure. Declining the king's invitation to sit beside him on the throne, he remained among his men. In hushed silence, the court heard the king's pronouncement. 'The lords of Carrion must pay three thousand marks in gold and silver for their crime. But because they have so gravely sinned, they must take up El Cid's challenge to a duel.'

The treacherous men rose to their feet in protest but they ranted and raved to no avail. The king's word was law.

At dawn next day the sun hardly shone on the steel of their lances as El Cid and Alvar Diaz rode out to the field of combat. Each faced his opponent, and galloped forward at full tilt.

Both struck the other's shield. Alvar Diaz drove through El Cid's defence but pierced no flesh. Unshaken from the blow, El Cid drove his lance through two folds of chain-mail, but the third held firm. So strong was the thrust, that mail and tunic, however, were driven a hand's breadth into the flesh, so that blood ran from Diaz's mouth and he was knocked to the ground, and forced to yield.

In the second joust, El Cid and Garcia Ordonez struck so hard with their spears that both were broken in two. Swiftly, El Cid took his sword, and split apart his foe's helmet, shearing the head-mail almost to the flesh. Terrified, Ordonez stumbled from the field. The Cid's honour was avenged.

El Cid wheeled about to
meet the enemy force,
and his men attacked
with such ferocity that
they overran the Moors.

There was panic on the battlefield as the great warrior rode among the Moors. A shower of arrows pierced his body, yet he did not flinch. He sat there straight and proud and unbending.

Not long after, El Cid returned to Valencia, but soon news came from across the sea that in the Sudan a Muslim tribe had launched a holy war. Under their chief, Yusuf, they had conquered the whole of North Africa. Now, invited by the Moorish kings of southern Spain, Yusuf had crossed the sea at the head of a huge army.

It was not long before Yusuf's battle drums were striking fear into the hearts of all Christians as the Muslims marched with the Moors against the armies of King Alfonso. A fateful battle took place at Sagrajas in the autumn of 1085; the Christian forces were utterly routed and survivors beheaded.

Yusuf's power quickly overran Moorish Spain. Then, with 50,000 men he marched on Valencia to do battle with El Cid. Yusuf's men pitched their tents around the town and began to beat their drums, terrifying Dona Jimena and her two daughters. But the good Cid stroked his beard and smiled. 'Have no fear. Within two weeks, the drums will be silent and hung in the church of Santa Maria.'

At the first Moorish charge El Cid's men rode from the city and fought bravely. They killed five hundred Moors that day before they retired. By the second cockcrow of the next day, El Cid charged out from the gates upon his steed, Babieca. He had 4,000 men against 50,000.

El Cid fought so fiercely with sword and lance, that no one could count the Moors he slew. Yet at the moment of his triumph, cruel fate struck. Just as the drum roll was muffled, as the battle cries ceased, an arrow pierced El Cid's strong chest. He knew that to remove the arrow would mean delay and the foe would capture the city. Already the Moors were proclaiming his death, regrouping for attack. They knew without their gallant leader the Christians were lost.

El Cid's life was ebbing fast. Riding to his wife at the edge of the battlefield, he kissed her and whispered his last daring plan. Then he died.

At once his grief-stricken wife and servants bound the dead Cid to his noble horse, strapped his sword to his hand, and turned him round to face the foe. Then Babieca galloped swiftly towards the fray.

'El Cid lives! We are doomed!' went up the cry.

It was just as El Cid had foretold. The Moors could not believe their eyes. The Cid was alive. He was immortal. There was panic on the battlefield as the great warrior rode among the Moors. A shower of arrows pierced his body, yet he did not flinch. He sat there straight and proud, unbending at the blows.

The enemy fled from the battle in disarray. They all took to their ships and sailed from Spain, never to invade again.

In some places, it is said that should Spain ever be in peril from a foreign force, El Cid will appear upon his noble steed, Babieca, and do battle again for the land he loves.

The Courage of Danko

This old Bessarabian legend was told to the Russian writer Maxim Gorky by an old women in Akkerman in 1894. Gorky writes that the purpose of such literature is 'to help people to know themselves, to strengthen their faith in themselves and their search for truth; to discover the good in people and erase the bad, to kindle shame, anger and courage in their hearts.'

Long, long ago on the borders of Turkey and the USSR, in a valley bounded on three sides by dense, tangled forests, and on the fourth by tall feather grass, there lived a band of people. They were a strong, brave and carefree group, bringing up their families in peace and comfort. But other tribes entered their valley and drove them out.

They had to take refuge in the forest or perish at the hands of the invading clans. But the forest was dark and dank and full of swamps. The foliage of the trees was so intertwined that it blocked out the sun; no light pierced the leafy canopy and reached down to the stagnant waters of the swamp.

As the people made their way forward deeper into the forest, cutting a path through vine and bramble, they breathed in the steaming vapours of the swamps, and many fell sick and died. Women and children cried in despair while the men brooded upon their fate. Their only hope was to find a way through the forest into the open plain beyond. Yet that meant braving the deathly bogs, cutting down the lofty trees whose gnarled, swarthy branches shut out the light and whose thick roots sank deep into the marshy soil.

The dense mass of trees stood still and silent in the murky gloom of daytime and seemed to press in upon the tribe at nightfall when the fires were lit. And always, day and night, shadows seemed to be waiting for a chance to pounce and suffocate them.

But they were a daring and courageous people, and they would willingly have turned back to fight their foes, even to the death. But they had to think of the future of the tribe; of their children and their ideals. They therefore sat dismally pondering their destiny throughout the long dark nights, amidst the stifling vapours of the swamp and the mournful song of the wind.

And as they sat there, the shadows of their fires leapt about them in a noiseless dance. Men and women grew weak from despair and the fear in their hearts. Many cowardly words were spoken, at first under the breath, then more openly as time went on. Some people were all for turning back and surrendering to their foes. Yet, at that fateful moment, a man came forward to help save the desperate tribe.

His name was Danko. He was young, handsome and brave. 'Stones do not move aside by brooding,' he said. 'Nor do prisoners enjoy freedom. Get up you men and women, and let us fight our way forward through this forest until we reach the open plain.'

The people gazed at him with renewed hope, seeing his eyes glow with life and strength. 'Lead on,' they said.

It was a hard and exhausting journey. At every step the unseen swamp swallowed people up; the giant trees barred their way and had to be hacked aside. The further they went, the trees grew thicker and their wills grew weaker. And soon some began to murmur against Danko, saying he was too young and headstrong; he had not earned the right to lead the tribe. Yet Danko kept walking boldly ahead, his purpose bright and clear.

One day a raging storm broke above the forest. In an instant the grey gloom had given way to blackest night. It was as if all the nights that had ever been now gathered beneath those ancient trees. Silently, the survivors of the tribe pushed on beneath the swaying trees, deafened by the roar of the storm and the

It was a hard and
exhausting journey. At
every step the unseen
swamp swallowed people
up; the giant trees barred
their way and had to be
hacked aside.

crashing thunder. Above the treetops flashed forked lightning, lighting up the forest for a moment in a chill-blue glow. It struck terror into everyone's hearts.

The people came to a halt, refusing to go on. Ashamed to admit their weakness to one another, they joined together in blaming Danko who was walking ahead. Angry cries rent the air above the storm.

'We cannot escape. This forest has no end!'

'You shall die for deceiving us!'

Danko turned to face them. 'But you told me to lead you. And I led you because I have the courage. But you? What have you done to help yourselves?'

His words enraged them even more. 'You shall die! You shall die!' they shrieked at him.

The forest roared its approval, echoing their cries as the lightning flashed. Danko gazed upon those for whom he had undertaken such a mission, and he saw they had become like wild beasts. He could see no mercy in their faces.

Resentment welled up in him. Yet he loved these people and he feared that without him they would all die. The flames of his burning urge to save them flared up in his heart and were reflected in his eyes, so that the people thought he was mad. And they drew warily back, expecting him to hurl himself against them. But then they closed around him so that they might seize him.

'What can I do to save these people?' cried Danko in despair above the sound of the storm. Then, before their terrified gaze, he flashed a knife. With it, he cut open his own breast, and with his bare hands he tore out his heart and held it high above his head. Yet he was unharmed.

The heart blazed more brightly than the sun, and the raging forest was lit up by it. The gloom receded into the yawning swamps of the forest, and in dumb amazement, the people stood as if turned to stone.

'Follow me,' cried Danko. And he dashed forward, holding the flaming heart above his head to light the way.

The people followed as if driven on. Once more the forest began to murmur and shake its fists in angry threat, but surely the people ran forward and the trees parted before the flaming heart. Even now there were those who fell by the wayside, but the people did not mourn for them this time. They had no thought but for the brave Danko rushing forward at their head.

All of a sudden, the dark-green forest wall moved aside, and Danko and his followers found themselves in a sea of sunlight and rainwashed air. The storm was now behind them over the forest, while here the sun shone down upon the plain. The earth throbbed with life, the grass bent forward under diamond raindrops and the nearby stream was streaked with gold.

Brave Danko cast his eye across the endless plain, over the land of freedom. His gaze swept over the happy people, then he sank to the ground and died.

His followers were so overjoyed at being free they did not even notice Danko's death. They did not see the brave heart burning beside the lifeless man. Only one frightened boy saw it, but, fearing what he did not understand, he stamped upon the flames to put them out. As he did so, a shower of blue and orange sparks surged up across the plain. That is why, before a storm, tongues of blue and orange flame may sometimes be seen in field and plain. A reminder of the man who gave up his own life to lead his people to freedom.

Siegfried the Dragonslayer

The story of Prince Siegfried and his heroic deeds is told in one of Germany's oldest poems, *Niebelungenlied*, or 'Song of the Niebelungs', written in about 1200 A.D. The poem tells of the royal family of Burgundy; King Gunter and his wife Queen Brunhild and Gunter's sister Kriemhild, who married Siegfried.

Although their story is full of adventure and excitement, it is also a tragic story, for in the end, Siegfried is murdered, and Kriemhild vows to get her revenge. As the second part of *Niebelungenlied* shows, it is a terrible revenge for it involves the destruction of the royal family of Burgundy and the death of Kriemhild herself.

When Siegfried was a young man, he left Xanten on the River Rhine, where his father King Siegmund was ruler, and set off to travel the world and seek adventure. It was not long before he found it. When he reached the Forest of Saxony, he came across a vast cave. Inside, there was a rich treasure which had once belonged to King Niebelung. No one, however, could reach the treasure because of the ferocious dragon who lived among the rocks above the cave. The dwarfs, who were guarding the treasure, were terrified of the dragon and the scorching flames it breathed from its mouth and nostrils whenever they tried to approach the cave.

The dwarfs begged Prince Siegfried to help them, and he agreed. To the amazement and delight of the dwarfs, Siegfried approached the dragon without showing any fear. Gripping his sword hilt firmly in his hand, he rushed towards the dragon and drove the sword deep into the creature's body.

Now that the dragon was dead, Siegfried bathed in its blood. This made him invincible, for now no blow could harm him–except in one place, on his back. While Siegfried was bathing a leaf fell from a linden tree and came to rest just below his left shoulder. The leaf prevented the dragon's blood reaching one small spot, so that here, Siegfried was unprotected.

The dwarfs, naturally, were delighted at Siegfried's great deed. 'Brave Prince,' they said, 'take this mighty sword Balmung, as your reward. A great hero deserves a mighty sword!'

Siegfried accepted the sword gladly, for it had a strong, finely-made blade. He also accepted the dwarfs' invitation to share out the treasure between the sons of King Niebelung.

Siegfried soon regretted doing so, because one of the Niebelung's sons accused him of cheating. The dwarfs sided with Niebelung's son and rushed at Siegfried. Siegfried was nearly overwhelmed, but fought back with all his strength and finally killed both Niebelung's sons and all the dwarfs.

Then, just as he thought he was finally free, Siegfried found himself attacked by an opponent he could not see. This invisible adversary struck at Siegfried over and over again, and just when Siegfried thought he knew where his attacker was, he was assaulted from another direction.

At last though, Siegfried managed to get hold of his attacker, who at once became visible. Siegfried was surprised to find he was holding a dwarf.

'Spare me, great Prince Siegfried, spare me!' begged the dwarf. 'Do not kill me! The treasure is yours now. I will guard it for you and give you a wonderful gift–but spare my life!'

The gift was indeed wonderful. It was a magic cape and anyone who wore it became invisible. Siegfried took it and also accepted an oath of loyalty from the dwarf, whose name was Alberich.

Leaving Alberich in charge of the treasure, Siegfried returned home to Xanten where his father greeted him as a great hero. King Siegmund held a big feast in his son's honour, and minstrels came to entertain the guests and sang songs of faraway places, of great heroes and beautiful maidens, like Princess Kriemhild of Burgundy. Kriemhild, sang the minstrels, was the loveliest princess in all the world. Siegfried was fascinated by her description and made up his mind to go to Burgundy and see her for himself.

Siegfried approached the
dragon without showing
any fear. Gripping his
sword hilt firmly in his
hand, he rushed towards
the dragon and drove the
sword deep into the
creature's body.

King Siegmund, however, tried to stop him. Kriemhild, Siegmund told his son, was guarded by her three brothers and their vassal Hagen von Tronje. The brothers—Gunter, Gernot and Giselher were all strong and powerful and their fame as heroes was almost as great as Siegfried's own. As for Hagen von Tronje, he was a dangerous ruffian. 'Do not go to Burgundy, my son,' begged King Siegmund. 'Stay here in Xanten and become king in my place.'

Siegfried, however, would not listen to his father. He was determined to meet Kriemhild. Accompanied by a guard of twelve men, he sailed up the Rhine from Xanten to the town of Worms in Burgundy, where the princess and her brothers lived in a fine palace.

King Gunter of Burgundy was a proud and powerful ruler and at first, he was angry that a stranger should sail into his realm without his permission. However, when he heard that his visitor was the famous hero, Siegfried, Gunter changed his mind and welcomed him as a friend.

To show how honoured they were by Siegfried's arrival, Gunter and his brothers spent all their time with him. They went hunting together, fought friendly jousts at tournaments and spent every night feasting and merrymaking. This went on for a year and though Siegfried enjoyed himself enormously, still he had not achieved his ambition of meeting the beautiful Princess Kriemhild. She remained shut away in her apartment, far beyond his reach.

Siegfried was about to give up and go home to Xanten when Burgundy was attacked by a huge army of Danes and Saxons, forty thousand strong. King Gunter was in great danger, for his forces consisted of only one thousand soldiers.

At once, Siegfried forgot about going home and offered to fight for Gunter

Siegfried managed to get hold of his attacker who at once became visible. Siegfried was surprised to find he was holding a dwarf.

and Burgundy. There were some fierce battles, but Siegfried was a mighty warrior and his sword Balmung, a powerful weapon. With Balmung, Siegfried helped defeat the invaders and personally took prisoner both the King of Denmark and the King of Saxony.

After this, King Gunter treated Siegfried with even greater respect and gave him the most important seat at the feast celebrating the victory. Better still, Gunter brought his sister Kriemhild to the banquet and as soon as he saw her, Siegfried realised that all he had heard about her was true. Everything about Kriemhild–her face, her figure, her smile, her manner–was just as lovely as Siegfried had imagined. As for Kriemhild, she was thrilled to meet Siegfried, whose deeds of valour she had long admired.

Siegfried and Kriemhild spent many happy days in each other's company, and within a short time they were deeply in love with each other. Siegfried made up his mind to ask Gunter for permission to marry Kriemhild, but before he could do so, the King confided to him that he, too, wished to marry. The bride Gunter wanted was Queen Brunhild of Iceland but, the King told Siegfried, it would not be easy for him to win her as his wife.

'Brunhild is extremely beautiful, but she is also very strong,' said Gunter. 'Only the man who can defeat her in a trial of strength will be allowed to marry her. I want to be that man. Will you come to Iceland and help me win Brunhild?'

It was a perilous quest, for if Gunter failed to defeat Brunhild, he would have to die. Siegfried decided he must help his friend, but first he wanted a promise from Gunter. 'I will go with you as long as you promise that I may wed Kriemhild,' Siegfried said.

Gunter gave Siegfried his promise and, taking with them a small force of soldiers, they sailed across the north Atlantic Ocean until they reached Iceland.

Queen Brunhild was angry, at first, when she learned that it was not the famous Siegfried the Dragonslayer who had come to fight for her hand in marriage. However, when she learned that King Gunter was her suitor, she agreed to hold a contest with him. But she warned Gunter: 'You and your men will lose your lives, for I am strong and determined.'

Now, Siegfried realised that Gunter would need a lot of help, for Brunhild was as powerful as the mightiest warrior. So, just before the contest began, Siegfried waited until he was alone and then put on the cloak of invisibility which the dwarf Alberich had given him. Then, unseen by anyone, Siegfried went to the place where the contest was being held.

The first part of the contest began. Gunter stood at one end of the field, holding his shield in front of him while Brunhild flung a huge javelin from the other end. The javelin came speeding towards Gunter and crashed right through his shield. The watching crowd expected to see Gunter fall dead from the blow, but to everyone's surprise, he was unharmed. Unseen, Siegfried had caught the javelin in mid-air and so reduced its force before it hit Gunter's shield. Then, as the crowd watched amazed, the javelin seemed to fling itself backwards, towards Brunhild. It hit her shield and split it apart. Siegfried, of course, had thrown the javelin back, but as no one could see him, it appeared as if the javelin had magic powers.

'Brunhild is extremely
beautiful, but she is also
very strong', said Gunter.
'Only the man who can
defeat her in a trial of
strength will be allowed
to marry her. I want to
be that man.'

Brunhild was enraged, but she was sure the next part of the contest would bring her success. She picked up a huge rock, threw it over a distance of 25 metres then with a single great leap, jumped on top of it. But once more, Gunter beat her. Siegfried, still invisible, threw the rock for him and it landed far beyond Brunhild's. Then, Siegfried lifted Gunter up and carried him all the way to where the rock lay.

King Gunter had won the contest and Brunhild had to agree to marry him. Though she did not, of course, know how Gunter had managed to score his victory, she was suspicious and thought, rightly, that somehow she had been tricked.

Gunter and Siegfried returned to Burgundy with Brunhild and there, two magnificent weddings were celebrated. King Gunter married Brunhild and Siegfried married his beautiful Kriemhild. Brunhild was still trying to puzzle out how Gunter had won where every other man had failed, and though she could not find an explanation, she decided to punish her new husband.

When they were alone in their bedchamber, Brunhild seized hold of Gunter with her powerful arms, tied him up with her girdle and then hung him on a hook on the wall. There, the furious Gunter had to stay all night.

The next night, Brunhild tried to tie up Gunter again, but suddenly, the girdle, together with her wedding ring, was snatched from her hands and vanished. Gunter had called on Siegfried once again, and Siegfried, hidden by his cloak of invisibility had come to the King's aid.

Afterwards, Siegfried returned to Kriemhild and gave her Brunhild's girdle and ring. He told her everything—how he had just frustrated Brunhild's plan and also how he had helped Gunter win the contest in Iceland. However, in telling his wife all this, Siegfried made a terrible mistake.

Brunhild, though, did not realise that she had been tricked again and settled down to a happy married life with her husband. Siegfried and Kriemhild, too, were very happy and there was much rejoicing when both couples produced sons.

Ten years went by, and in Xanten, Kriemhild began to feel homesick. So, Siegfried took her on a visit to Burgundy. Gunter and his sister were very pleased to see each other again after such a long time but before long, Kriemhild and Brunhild began to quarrel. Brunhild thought her sister-in-law had become far too proud and haughty. Kriemhild grew even more proud when Siegfried scored triumph after triumph at the tournaments which Gunter held in his honour.

'My Siegfried is the greatest of all heroes and warriors!' Kriemhild exclaimed. 'He is greater than any man alive.'

Brunhild was enraged, because this seemed to be a great insult to her own husband.

Then, when the royal family went to church, Brunhild became even more angry because Kriemhild tried to go through the door first.

'How dare you go before me!' stormed Brunhild. 'My husband is the King. You are only the wife of his vassal. I must enter the church first!'

Instead of standing aside for the Queen, Kriemhild burst out laughing. 'Gunter is your husband only because of what Siegfried did for him' she told

Brunhild. 'You have no reason to be proud. They made a fool of you!'

Then, Kriemhild told the Queen everything–how Siegfried had helped Gunter in Iceland and also how he had defeated her plan to tie up Gunter with her girdle. As proof, Kriemhild showed Brunhild her girdle and ring.

Brunhild was speechless with rage and shame. If the truth ever got out, she thought, everyone would laugh at her. Brunhild went to Gunter and forced him to question Siegfried in her presence. Siegfried swore an oath to tell the truth, but, he lied. Brunhild was not satisfied. She vowed to get her revenge.

Brunhild asked Hagen von Tronje, Gunter's cruel vassal, to help her. Hagen agreed and together they plotted the downfall of Siegfried. First, Hagen went to Kriemhild and told her a story about a new war between Burgundy and Denmark and Saxony. The battles would be very fierce, Hagen said, and Siegfried would be in great danger so if Kriemhild would sew a yellow cross over the place where Siegfried was not protected by the dragon's blood, Hagen would make sure that place was not exposed to enemy swords.

Kriemhild was very frightened, and did as Hagen had asked. She was very relieved, though, when shortly afterwards, news came that the Danes and Saxons had decided not to fight and had gone home. (The Danes and Saxons, of course, had never left home, because Hagen had made up the whole story.)

Siegfried, however, had wanted to fight in the war and now felt restless and frustrated. So, Hagen persuaded Gunter to hold a hunting expedition to enable Siegfried and his other commanders to get over their disappointment.

Kriemhild, meanwhile, had begun to suspect a plot and she begged Siegfried not to attend the hunt. She was sure something terrible was going to happen.

'You speak nonsense, my love,' Siegfried told Kriemhild. 'I am strong and powerful and I shall be among my friends.'

The hunt took place at Odenwald and the hunters chased their prey with great energy. When the time came to rest and eat their meal, they found, however, that there was no wine. Hagen had arranged this.

'Let us drink water, then,' Hagen suggested. 'We can race each other to the stream over there!'

Hagen and King Gunter began to run towards the stream and Siegfried followed. When he reached the bank, Siegfried laid his sword and spear on one side and bent over the water to drink. This was just the moment Hagen had been waiting for. He rushed up behind Siegfried, snatched up the spear and struck Siegfried just where Kriemhild's yellow cross showed on his shirt. The spear went deep and pierced Siegfried's heart. He tried to get up, but he was too badly wounded. He fell to the ground and moments later, was dead.

When Kriemhild heard the news, her cries of sorrow could be heard all over the city of Worms. She was certain that her husband had been murdered for Hagen von Tronje had been boasting of how he had killed him. Even so, Kriemhild wanted proof. So, she watched carefully as Brunhild and Hagen came to the church where Siegfried's body lay. As they approached the coffin, Siegfried's wounds began to bleed.

Now, Kriemhild had her proof and she swore an oath that she would make Brunhild and Hagen suffer for their terrible crime. 'Even if it costs me my life,' Kriemhild vowed. 'My Siegfried will be avenged.'

King Arthur and The Round Table

The legends of King Arthur and The Knights of the Round Table are amongst the oldest and most popular of all the legends of Britain. These tales of adventure and romance have been told many times both in prose and poetry, by poets and storytellers such as Dryden, Swinburne and Tennyson. But the most famous and most consulted Arthurian narrative of all is the *Morte d'Arthur* of Sir Thomas Malory written over five hundred years ago. The following story tells of the formation of the Knighthood of the Round Table.

Now that Arthur's realm was at peace and free of his enemies, there were many barons who pressed him to take a wife. In all things Arthur was guided by Merlin's counsel, so one time he asked his friend, 'My barons are eager for me to take a wife so that they might have a queen; what is your advice?'

'They are right,' said Merlin. 'A man of your position should not be without a wife, nor should the realm be without a queen. Tell me, is there anyone you love above all others?'

'Yes,' said Arthur without a pause, 'I love my lady Guenevere, daughter of King Leodegrance of the land of Camelard; he who owns the Round Table that my father Uther gave him. Guenevere is the fairest, kindest lady in all the world.'

Merlin was evidently troubled. For he could see that this course threatened stormy times ahead.

'Certainly she is very lovely,' he said. 'Had you not loved her as you do, I would have found you a wife that would love and please you well. Your union with Guenevere may one day bring your downfall and that of the kingdom. However, since your heart is set, I shall arrange the marriage.'

So Merlin went to King Leodegrance and told him of Arthur's wish to seek his daughter's hand.

'This is the most welcome news I have ever heard,' said the king. 'That so noble and brave a man as King Arthur should wish to wed my daughter pleases me greatly. I shall send him a gift that will please him above all others: the Round Table given to me by Uther Pendragon.'

King Leodegrance entrusted his daughter Guenevere to Merlin, and the Round Table too, and they returned by land and water to King Arthur's court at Camelot. Arthur was overjoyed and made arrangements for the wedding to be held at Whitsuntide.

Meanwhile, much pleased with the Round Table, Arthur bade Merlin choose fifty knights, the worthiest in the realm, to take their places at the Table. Within a short time Merlin had gathered at court forty-six men, the bravest and most valiant knights in all the land.

At Whitsuntide the Archbishop of Canterbury journeyed to Camelot to marry King Arthur and the Lady Guenevere in the Church of St. Stephen. The knights cheered as the magnificent ceremony ended with peals of bells ringing out all over Camelot.

As they left the church Arthur asked the Archbishop to come with them to the court and to bless each seat at the Round Table. As each place was blessed with due solemnity, a knight took that seat, until all the places were filled save four.

When all the knights were seated around the Table, and Arthur and Guenevere had taken their place at the high table, Merlin addressed them thus: 'Sir knights, stand now and bow to your king and queen.'

As each knight did so, letters of gold mysteriously appeared on his chair, spelling out the name of the knight whose place it was.

'I shall now explain the wonders of the Round Table,' said Merlin. 'At this Table, no man can complain that he is at the head or foot, lower or higher

He opened the door for
Sir Pellinor, who knelt
before King Arthur, then
took his seat at the table.

than another. Every man is equal. And when a knight is slain in battle, a new knight will take his place and have his name inscribed upon the chair. The names of all the knights who sit at King Arthur's Table will live forever.'

'But four seats remain unfilled,' broke in King Arthur. 'For whom are they intended?'

'One place is for your recent foe, the bold Sir Pellinor, who waits outside,' replied Merlin.

With that he opened the door for Sir Pellinor, who knelt before King Arthur, then took his seat at the Table.

'Two more are for two of the bravest knights in the kingdom who are not yet come,' continued Merlin. 'As for the one remaining, that is the Perilous Seat. Only on pain of death shall that seat be taken by any man save he for whom it is intended. And he will be the best knight of them all.'

Merlin looked so stern that none of the knights, not even Arthur, dared ask Merlin who was the best knight of them all.

Then Arthur looked at his knights seated round the Table, and said, 'You must swear that you will never act unfairly, never in any way be unjust, and always show mercy to those who ask you for it. If you break your vow you must forfeit your place at the Round Table. Further, knights of my court, you must always be chivalrous to women, rich or poor. Do not battle without good cause, and never for worldly goods.'

This was the vow taken by all the Knights of the Round Table. And every year they renewed their vow at the high festival of Whitsuntide.

Robin Hood Meets Little John & Friar Tuck

Only the stories of King Arthur rival those of Robin Hood in British legend and folklore. Robin Hood, like Arthur, may or may not once have lived. But his heroic story, which first appeared in medieval writings and ballads, has been passed down through the ages, and is today as fresh and evergreen as it was in the century after the Norman conquest, when his exploits took place.

Robin knew many of the forests in the far north, especially those near his home at Hartoft, but Sherwood was new to him and it took him some time to learn its glades and rides and tracks and how the rivers flowed through it on their journey to the sea.

One day he came to a stream with a narrow bridge across it, just a few poles lashed together, almost too narrow for one man to cross, let alone two. Just as he was stepping on to it, a huge black-bearded fellow with shoulders like an ox came out of the trees on the other side, carrying an oak staff six feet long.

'I'll trouble you to step aside 'till I have crossed,' he shouted to Robin as he came up to the bridge.

'I turn aside for no man,' answered Robin. 'Hereabouts men turn aside for me.'

'Then let us try the matter with our staves,' said the bearded fellow. 'Let him who throws the other in the stream have right of way.'

'Gladly,' replied Robin. 'But give me time to cut a staff.' And he drew his sword and hacked a branch from an ash tree that grew nearby and trimmed it of leaves and twigs. Then threw down his bow and sword and quiver.

Stepping on to the bridge together, one at either end, they advanced to meet each other. Robin, being light and quick, made the first stroke, aiming it high to crack the bearded fellow's head. Black-beard warded off the blow and in his turn gave Robin a great thwack on his left arm, nearly breaking it. 'Hello,' thought Robin, as they locked staves and tried to overset each other into the stream, 'I've got my hands full here.'

Then he gave Black-beard a rap across his ear that made it sing, and followed it with another on his staff, nearly knocking it out of his hand. Indeed, Robin used every trick he knew, but Black-beard laughed and parried every stroke. So they moved backwards and forwards, first one gaining the advantage then the other, until at last, advancing to the middle of the bridge, Black-beard gave Robin an upward blow that lifted him into the air, right off the bridge and splash, head over heels into the water!

As Robin looked up, streaming wet, the bearded fellow was laughing and offering his staff to haul him back on to dry land. There Robin embraced him. 'You beat me fair and square,' he said. 'I dub you King of the Quarterstaff. What is your name and where do you come from?'

'John Little is my name,' said the bearded giant. 'I come from west of here, from Hathersage. I was caught poaching in the farmer's fishpond. Five or six set on me and beat me black and blue. But I gave better than I got. I broke a head or two, and learning that you welcome outlaws hereabouts, I started walking east and here I am.' Then he laid his huge hand on Robin's shoulder. 'You have a mighty heart inside that slender body.' And they clasped hands and swore to be friends, and John Little became Robin's right-hand man.

'But we must change your name,' said Robin. 'John Little falls awkwardly from the tongue and no way suits your bulk. I shall re-christen you. Henceforth be Little John.'

So Little John joined the band and the outlaws welcomed him as gladly as they had welcomed Robin. He was so brave and strong and, next to Robin, the finest bowman. He was six feet seven inches tall and his bow four inches

A huge black-bearded
fellow with shoulders like
an ox came out of the
trees on the other side,
carrying an oak staff six
feet long.

longer, the longest longbow ever made. He could shoot fourteen or fifteen arrows in a minute, the fastest archer in the land save Robin. Not shooting wildly but all aimed and all clapped squarely in the clout, which is the bowman's target.

The longbow was a terrible weapon. Well-aimed arrows flew fast and true, and their hardened points had such hitting power that they could pierce a knight's armour a hundred yards away. At famous battles like Crécy and Poitiers and Agincourt, a small force of two hundred and fifty archers could shoot eighty thousand arrows within half an hour. These fighting archers wore no armour, only a strong leather cap. And they had no horses to bother with, so they could move lightly and swiftly; and often one of their arrows would go right through a knight and his horse and be sticking out on the other side.

For two hundred years, until the coming of gunpowder, the longbow was the master of the battlefield. And the English were the masters of the longbow. Children were taught to use it from an early age and laws were passed which said that every man and boy must practise shooting every week.

A few weeks after Little John joined the outlaws Robin found the very man he was looking for to be their priest. His name was Michael Tuck, a monk from Fountains Abbey near to Ripon. To understand the meaning of the words 'monk' and 'abbey', it is necessary to know something about the Church in Robin's time and how the Christian story had got twisted out of shape and how men often used it in the wrong way.

The story taught that God had sent Jesus down to earth to help people out of their troubles and to heal them when they were sick and encourage them to live better lives. He and his disciples were a tiny team and he was their captain. And when he was crucified his eleven disciples tried to carry on his work. But they feared that when their own turn came to die his teachings would be forgotten and it would be as if he had never lived.

For a long time they tried to go on living holy lives all by themselves, in huts and caves and even on top of marble columns. Then they thought that if they formed themselves into fresh teams and built places called abbeys where each team could be together, their singing and praying would be stronger than if they lived separately. Besides, they would no longer be lonely. And this idea spread all over Europe and hundreds of these abbeys came to be built. And the men who lived in them were called monks and when they joined they had to promise to obey the abbey rules and live like Jesus had done, praying and teaching and healing the sick.

Each abbey had a big church for singing and praying in, and a dining room for eating and a dormitory for sleeping: also a kitchen and a pantry and an infirmary and a guest house and workshops and storerooms and so on; everything they could possibly need.

Some of the monks spent their whole lives worshipping God at special times all through the day and night while their helpers worked in the gardens and orchards or out on the hills looking after the sheep. Sometimes there were over a hundred praying monks and five hundred working ones in a single abbey. And every abbey had a high wall round it. It was like a complete village without any women or children living in it. Only men.

The one in charge of the abbey, the sort of headmaster, was called the abbot. He had a lodging all to himself. And there were special rules for how the monks should live, when they should pray and when they should eat and sleep and when they should work in the fields and so on. And they all dressed alike in rough woollen gowns and woollen stockings, with a rope or leather girdle round their waist. And a circle of hair in the middle of their heads was shaved off as a sort of trade mark.

Now as time went on, many of these abbeys forgot all about Jesus and his teachings. They only wanted to get richer and have more power over people's lives. And one of the richest and most powerful in the whole of England was this one called Fountains in Yorkshire. And it was from Fountains that Michael Tuck had run away and was now living by himself in a little cave in the middle of Sherwood Forest.

Michael was the son of a butcher in the village of Pately Bridge and when he was seventeen years old he joined the Abbey as a novice, which is someone who goes in to be trained. And in time he became a full-fledged monk and he was a hard worker and a good strong singer and a deep believer and a credit to the Abbey.

But one day he asked why abbeys needed to become so rich and powerful and why they needed to steal whole villages from the poor and break up their families and turn them out to starve. 'Is that what Jesus meant when he said, "Another commandment I give unto you. Love one another"?' he asked.

When he heard what Michael had been saying the Abbot got very angry and had him brought up in front of the court which met every morning in a part of the Abbey called the Chapter House.

But Michael wouldn't give in. He said he thought that many abbeys had strayed a long way from the truth and that Fountains was just as bad as some of the others. In fact he said he thought it had become very greedy and had forgotten all the wonderful things Jesus had taught. And he said he thought it ought to pull its socks up before it was too late. At this the Abbot went very red in the face and tried to hit Michael with his crozier. But Michael ducked and that made the Abbot lose his balance and fall over. And when they had picked him up and dusted him down and put him back on his throne, he said that as a punishment for saying such wicked things Michael must be shut away in the Abbey prison for three months with nothing but bread and water to eat and drink. And six monks tried to lay hold of him and take him to the prison and lock him in.

But Michael was very strong and he fought them off and knocked them flying and ran from the Chapter House and escaped into the country, travelling South and finally settling all by himself in a little cave beside a stream in Sherwood Forest, resisting anyone who tried to shift him. He did not hate the Abbot or the monks. Indeed, he felt sorry for them because he knew they had their minds fixed on the wrong things, that they were wanting to get rich instead of staying poor as Jesus had said they must if they wanted to serve God properly. But now let us get back to our story.

One day Robin came to a river he would have to cross if he was to be back in camp by supper time. But after the September rains it was swollen so high and rushing along so fast that at first he thought the only possible way to cross would be to jump in and swim.

Then he noticed a strange figure sitting on the bank dressed in a rough brown habit with sandals on his feet. By his side lay his bow and quiver and his broadsword, and he was fishing with a net on the end of a long pole. It was Michael fishing for his supper.

When he saw how broad and strong he looked, Robin said to himself, 'Here's a man strong enough to carry me across—with luck I shouldn't even get my feet wet!' So he walked up to Michael and tapped him on the shoulder.

'Fellow,' he said. 'You fish in outlaw waters. The fish you catch belong by rights to us. But if you carry me to the other side we will give you permission to fish our rivers once a month.'

'I take only what I need for food,' replied Michael bluntly. 'The fish and fowl are free. But I will carry you across. Climb on my back and mind you hold your bow and quiver high.' Then he took off his sandals and stockings and tucked his skirts up into his belt, and Robin climbed onto him pick-a-back fashion. And Michael waded into the water, buffeting it aside with lusty sinews, finally setting Robin down on the opposite bank as dry as a bone.

Now Michael did not like the way Robin had spoken to him. He had as much right to fish the stream as anyone else and he certainly was not going to ask permission from a bunch of outlaws. So he thought he would pay Robin out and this is how he did it.

'You look a strong young fellow,' he said. 'Do you think you could carry me across as easily as I carried you? If you can, I will bring you back and set you down on this side once again. There now! I challenge you!'

Robin had never yet refused to accept a challenge, so he laid aside his bow and quiver and came to the water's edge. Then took Michael on his back and stepped into the water.

He could tell by looking at him that Michael was pretty heavy, but as they moved towards the middle of the stream he seemed to grow heavier still so that, with the water rushing past, it was as much as he could do to keep his feet, and the sweat poured down his forehead and he was soon puffing and blowing like a grampus. But at last he staggered up the opposite bank and set Michael down.

'There,' he said. 'You thought I'd never do it. Now comes your turn. Carry me back and set me on my way!'

Once more Michael waded into the stream, carrying Robin as easily as if he were a two-year-old. But suddenly, giving a great jerk of his spine and shaking Robin's arms from round his neck, he hurled him three or four feet into the air and splash, head over ears into the river!

Robin fell face downwards and disappeared from view and it was some seconds before he managed to get his head above water again. When he did so, coughing and spluttering, he saw Michael standing up to his waist in the stream shaking with laughter.

'You say I must beg leave to come a-fishing in your brook,' said Michael. 'Must I now beg leave to fish you out?' And he put his great foot on Robin's chest, holding him firmly in the water.

Robin had never yet
refused to accept a
challenge, so he laid aside
his bow and quiver and
came to the water's edge.
Then he took Michael on
his back and stepped into
the water.

'No,' shouted Robin in return. 'You can come fishing when you will. I give you best.' So Michael bent down and hauled him up on to the bank. Then, still laughing, helped him squeeze the water out of his clothes.

'I fancy you had better get before a fire before you take a chill,' he said. 'Be on your way and God go with you.'

'You must come too,' said Robin. 'Our camp is but a mile or two from here. My outlaws are good men and true. We need a priest.' Then, as he waited for Michael to answer, 'What must we call you?'

'My name is Michael. Michael Tuck. Lately of Fountains Abbey. I quarrelled with the Abbot and we parted company. Since then I have lived alone, here in the greenwood.'

'Come join with me and my brave company,' said Robin, holding out his hand. 'We miss the word of God. We miss the bread and wine.' And he took Michael's huge hand and shook it and they swore to be friends. That was one of the nicest things about Robin. He never minded being beaten. At one time or another he fought with a butcher, a potter, a tanner, a tinker, a shepherd, and a Yorkshire pindar and was beaten by them all. But he soon shook hands and praised the men who had beaten him. That is why his men loved him and that is why he gathered together such a strong and loyal band and that is why he was such a great leader.

So Michael joined the outlaws. They made him a tiny chapel in the greenwood, with an altar and a cross. And the morning after he came, he said Mass and the outlaws all knelt down and he went from man to man with the wine cup, and Clement Glose made up a platter of bread cut into tiny pieces and every man took bread and wine in memory of the little supper that the greatest of all outlaws had shared with his twelve comrades long long ago, in an upper room in old Jerusalem.

And Tricket sat at the end of the line looking up with her great brown eyes, so she had a morsel of bread and a sip of wine along with the others, because Jesus loved animals as well as men and women. Indeed, if he and his mother had not escaped to Egypt on a donkey, King Herod might have killed him when he was a tiny baby.

At the end of his life he rode into Jerusalem on another donkey as if to say thank you to all donkeys. Some people say that the second donkey was the son of the one his mother had used to carry him safely into Egypt all those years ago. And others say that he meant to put an extra verse into the Beatitudes, 'Blessed are the animals for they are as important as man, and deserve to be loved and cared for.' But he forgot.

In later days monks who left their monasteries and went about the countryside doing good and helping people like Jesus had done were called 'Friars', which means 'Brothers'. But that is exactly what Michael had been doing for twenty years and more, here in the greenwood. So he was the first to think of it. That is why he is always known as 'Friar Tuck' instead of 'Brother Michael'.

Beowulf the Chieftain

The oldest of the great poems written in English, *Beowulf* was probably composed in the first half of the eighth century, but was preserved in a late tenth-century manuscript found in the south of the kingdom of the West Saxons. In 1731, before any translation of the text from Old English (or Anglo-Saxon) into modern English, it was badly damaged by fire which destroyed several lines. Shortly afterwards, an Icelander, Thorkelin came to England to copy out the manuscript which was published in 1815.

While the three-thousand line poem is English, it deals with the Scandinavian ancestors of the English–the Danes and Geats. The story refers to history some two hundred years before the poem was written–a time following the first invasion of England by Germanic tribes in 449. The audience to which the poem was sung was probably of the same Geatish stock as the hero Beowulf.

Through the dark night slid the fierce, evil shadow of Grendel, rover of the borders, master of the moors, fens and fields, an unhappy creature, from whom sprang all cruel deeds, trolls, elves, monsters and giants. He hated the laughter of men, the sound of the harp and the minstrel's song that echoed from the great feasting hall of Heorot.

Finest folk-hall on middle-earth, Heorot was home of the great chieftain of the Danes, Hrothgar, and his band of warriors. Each day the tall, wide-gabled hall would echo to their merry-making and, later to their happy snores. It was while the men were sleeping one night, Grendel first came to Heorot and savagely killed thirty thanes. First light revealed the slaughter. The old chieftain and his men were grief-stricken. Yet after that night, Grendel returned several times to kill even more. Ruthless, he also lay in wait for warriors, young and old, as they crossed the misty moors.

So great was the Danes' despair, it broke their spirit. What could they do against the terrible creature? Meanwhile, across the sea, in the land of the Geats, a young thane heard of Grendel's cruelty. His name was Beowulf, and no-one was stronger, more noble or great. He gathered together fourteen chosen warriors and set off, in a wooden ship, to help the old war-chief. On the second day, the seafarers sighted cliffs. As the men of the Geats stepped ashore, the coastguard rode down from the clifftop, shouting: 'Who are you, warriors, dressed in armour, with shining shields?'

'We are Geats,' said Beowulf, 'friends of the Danes.'

'Go forward then,' replied the coastguard. 'I'll guard your boat.' And he showed them the path that led to Heorot.

The fifteen Geat warriors followed the track inland until, at sunset, they came to the timbered hall of the Danish chief. As ordered, they placed their war-shields and wooden spears against the wall outside, before entering. Followed by his men, Beowulf approached the spot where Hrothgar sat with his company of earls. 'Hail, Hrothgar,' said Beowulf. 'I am a thane of the Geat chieftain Hygelac. I have heard of Grendel and that this hall is unsafe after dark.'

'Greetings, Beowulf. You are welcome. But how can you help us?' asked old Hrothgar.

'I will rid Heorot of Grendel. It is said the monster uses no weapons, so nor will I. I will fight him with my bare hands.'

The hall echoed with loud cheers. A table was cleared for the fifteen Geats, and food and drink were served. Finally, Hrothgar rose and wished Beowulf good luck. 'Never before, since I could raise my hand and shield, have I entrusted this hall to a stranger,' said the old Chieftain. 'Guard it well, Beowulf.' Then Hrothgar and his warriors left the hall for the safety of the houses beyond.

Meanwhile, Beowulf removed his armour and helmet, handed his iron sword to a fellow Geat, and lay down to rest. Each man found himself a sleeping place, though none believed he would see the dawn or ever return home. Then from the moor, below the misty hills, Grendel approached. Beneath the dark clouds, he moved stealthily until he reached Heorot. The door was bolted. Furiously, Grendel tore it open to stand within the hall. Staring with a fiery

Staring with a fiery gaze, Grendel saw the Geats were all sleeping. But Beowulf watched through half-closed eyes. Next moment, Grendel clutched a sleeping man and killed him.

gaze, he saw the Geats were all sleeping. But Beowulf watched through half-closed eyes. Next moment, Grendel clutched a sleeping man and killed him. Still the other Geats slept. Grendel stepped among them, this time reaching for Beowulf. In a flash, he leapt up, seizing the monster's hand in a vice-like grip. Never on middle-earth had Grendel met such strength and, shocked, he tried to run. But he could not break free for Beowulf held him firmly. As Beowulf wrestled with the evil monster and gripped even harder, the hall rang with furious cries. By now all Beowulf's men were awake, swords drawn, striking at Grendel to protect their chief. At last, mortally wounded by Beowulf, Grendel fled into the night to die.

Returning to the hall next morning, led by their aged chieftain, the Danish warriors marvelled at what had happened. Soon others came from near and far to wonder and all agreed that Beowulf was the greatest of men.

But they celebrated too soon. For while they slept in Heorot that night, Grendel's mother came to avenge his death and claim another victim. Beowulf, who by chance had slept in an outhouse was quickly fetched. 'I promise you that wherever she goes, I will hunt her down,' he told Hrothgar.

So he set out with his own men and accompanied by a band of Danes. They followed the tracks of Grendel's mother through the forest and across the moor, over steep rocky slopes, narrow paths and into unfamiliar land. They passed stagnant pools—the lairs of water demons—and at last reached a cold sinister wood standing high above a lake. Beowulf pulled on his armour and helmet and held Hrunting, his iron-edged sword. Then, as a horn sang out its war song, he dived into the lake.

For half a day he swam down and down, seeking the lake-bed, which was the monster's lair. As he reached it, Grendel's mother trapped him in her crushing grip. But she could not pierce Beowulf's armour. So the ogress swept him even deeper into a bright, dry, firelit hall. Struggling free, Beowulf drew his sword and struck at his evil enemy. But its blows could not wound her. Beowulf spotted a sword upon the rock wall. It was an old blade made by giants, larger than any man, save Beowulf, could hold. Dashing across the floor, he seized its hilt and, with one last effort, swung the blade with all his strength. It struck the she-monster and she crashed lifelessly to the ground.

As Beowulf's men watched the lake, and its waters seethe and boil, they sighed, fearing the worst. Yet they waited. Just as the men turned to go, the water parted and out stepped their leader. When Beowulf told them what had happened, they returned to Heorot in high spirits. There, Hrothgar embraced Beowulf warmly. 'My friend,' he said, 'stay here always.'

'Thank you, chieftain,' said Beowulf, 'but it is time my warriors and I went home. Yet if ever you should need us, send word and we shall come.'

And so they departed. On the sand, their boat was ready, loaded with Hrothgar's gifts. The old coastguard who had stood watch helped them to launch the ship and it was soon cutting across the water. So the wind carried it, until the fourteen men sighted the white headlands of the Geats.

As for Beowulf, he was destined for many great deeds. But when at last he died, chieftain of the Geats, men said that he was, among world chiefs, the mildest and kindest to his people.

Deirdre of the Sorrows

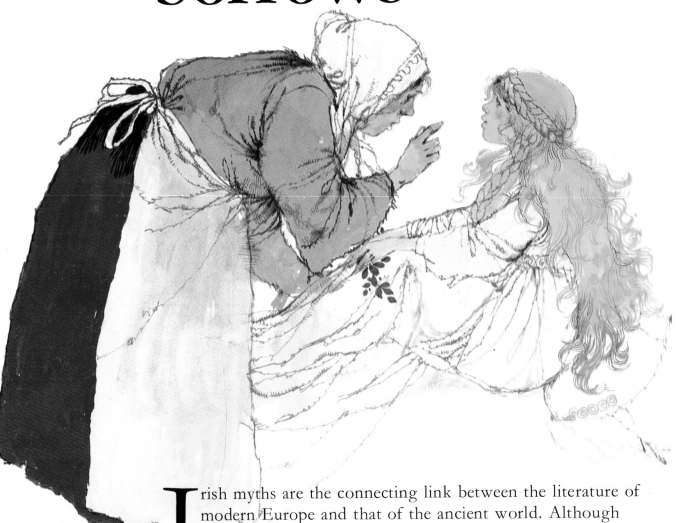

Irish myths are the connecting link between the literature of modern Europe and that of the ancient world. Although written tales date back to about the seventh century, the earliest surviving manuscripts belong to the 1100s and includes Deirdre, said by some to be the 'most stunning tale ever written in Irish.' The story is repeated in a fourteenth century manuscript called *Leabhar Buidhe Leacain* or *Yellow Book of Lecan*.

Originally the tale, like all Irish myths, was recited and written in verse. Although the first title was *The Exile of the Sons of Usna*, it is better known as the story of *Deirdre*, and served as the inspiration for Yeats' play and James Stephens' novel, both of that title, plus J. M. Synge's play, *Deirdre of the Sorrows*.

While a storm raged, Conor, chieftain of Ulster, and his Red Knights feasted with their host, a minstrel named Felim, whose wife was about to have a child. Cathub, the wise druid, stepped forward saying, 'The child will be a girl. When she grows up she shall have long golden hair, calm grey-green eyes, cheeks as pink as foxgloves and snow-white teeth. So lovely will she be, that queens will be jealous and, kings will go to war for her. Her fame and beauty will lead to great suffering in this realm, and the Red Knights will die by each other's hand.'

Shortly afterwards, a servant hurried in, bringing news of the baby girl's birth. 'She will grow up under my protection. And when the time comes, she will be my queen,' announced Conor.

The others did not dare argue, though they feared the prophecy. But boldly Cathub said, 'You will regret this, Conor. She will bring sadness. Therefore folk will know her as Deirdre of the Sorrows.'

When Deirdre was old enough, Conor took her from her parents and sent her to a castle deep in the forest. No-one else was allowed to enter, except some servants and Lebarcham, an old nurse, who was to be her tutor.

Occasionally, Conor visited, and saw Deirdre growing into a maid as lovely as Cathub had foretold. In the forest castle, Conor hoped to keep her safe from the prophecy.

One winter's day, when Deirdre was sixteen, she glanced down from her window on to the snowy courtyard, where the servants had killed a calf and a hungry raven pecked at blood-spots in the snow. 'I would love a man of those three colours,' she said to Lebarcham. 'Hair raven black, cheeks bright-red and skin as white as snow.'

'Then bad luck will befall you,' replied the nurse. 'You are promised to the chieftain, and he would surely kill you and your beloved if he were crossed.'

'I had a dream last night' continued Deirdre, 'that I will marry such a man as I have spoken of, and not the chieftain, who is old and ugly.' The nurse thought for a moment, then said, 'Naisi, one of Usna's sons has raven-black hair, red cheeks and pure-white skin. He and his two brothers live nearby.'

Now Naisi and his brothers, Aindle and Arddan, were best loved of all the Red Knights of Ulster. They were brave and strong in war, fair and just in peace, and swift as a deer when hunting. Naisi was the greatest of Ulster's young chieftains and, a gifted minstrel as well. He loved to wander, play his harp and sing. And everyone who heard his song forgot their worries.

One day, as Naisi sat alone in a forest glade near the secret castle, he had no idea a maiden watched him. He sang so sweetly that even the birds listened. In her lonely castle, Deirdre had caught the faint sound of Naisi's voice and had crept out, towards the glade. Instantly, she fell in love with Naisi and said, 'I choose you.'

Though stunned by Deirdre's beauty, he was wary of the prophesy, for he recognised her from the many stories he had heard. 'Hush, I am not afraid of Conor, but you have to be his bride. I would not bring suffering upon the Ulster men.' But, crying, Deirdre moved him so deeply that finally Naisi agreed to marry her. Much as he loved Deirdre he felt sad and apprehensive. Then,

picking up his harp, he began to sing a wistful, yet happy song. His voice carried above the trees to his brothers. When they learned of Naisi's decision, Aindle and Arddan warned, 'No good can come of this. All the same, we will stand by you. We must leave our homes and seek safety elsewhere in Erin.' So that night they departed with their followers. Deirdre went too.

For a while Usna's three sons found protection with other chieftains. But such was Conor's anger that finally none dared to shelter them.

Then the fugitives had to leave Erin and cross the sea to Albu where they settled in the wild glens, built homes on the mountainside, and hunted deer and boar. Sometimes they raided cattle belonging to the men of Albu and it was not long before they were at war with the Albu tribes. But eventually an agreement was made with the Albu chieftain and Usna's sons moved to the green lowlands near the chief's own castle. Remembering the prophecy, they built their houses in a circle hoping to stop the chieftain's men from spotting Deirdre. For they feared more killing on her account.

Early one morning, however, the chieftain's steward came to summon the sons to court. Since they were away hunting, he entered Naisi's house and saw Deirdre asleep on her bed. Amazed by her beauty, he hurried back to tell the chieftain. 'At last,' he told his lord, 'we have found a woman worthy of you.' So the Albu chief cunningly tried to think of ways to dispose of Usna's sons. He sent them into battle and on dangerous missions. Yet they always returned.

In desperation, the chief decided to send his army to capture Deirdre. But learning of the attack, the brothers fled with her in the night, taking refuge on a lonely island in the western sea.

Meanwhile, back in Erin, news of Deirdre and the sons of Usna had reached Conor and his Red Knights at the castle of Emain Macha. There were many among them who missed the good, brave brothers, and said so. 'Pardon them, Conor, and let them come home to Ulster'. Conor stroked his beard, deep in thought. At last he agreed. 'Send word to them.'

Deirdre had caught the faint sound of Naisi's voice and had crept out towards the glade. Instantly, she fell in love with Naisi and said, 'I choose you.'

'But whom would they trust?' asked a knight. 'They might think it a trick to lure them to their death.' In fact, that was what Conor planned. His hatred of the brothers had not faded, and he still hoped to marry Deirdre.

'Then take a message to Naisi,' he said, 'and have him name three men he will accept as guarantees of safety.' The men of Ulster were delighted at the thought of the three knights' return. And it was not long before a message came from Usna's sons, naming three men they trusted: Fergus, Dubthach and Cormac.

So these three were sent, and Conor pledged that no harm would come to the sons of Usna, while they were in the three men's keeping. But when they had sailed for the western isle, where Naisi and his brothers were, Conor spoke quietly to Borrach whose castle of Dun Borrach stood above the harbour. 'When their ship arrives,' he said, 'invite Fergus, Dubthach and Cormac to feast and stay with you, but send the sons of Usna straight to me. I will welcome them first.' Only too well Conor knew that a Red Knight was duty-bound to accept an invitation to another's castle. Fergus, Dubthach and Cormac would go with Borrach and the sons of Usna would lose their protective escort. The Ulster chieftain could then deal with them as he chose.

As Fergus, Dubthach and Cormac drew near to the island, Fergus let out a hunting call. Echoing across the water, it reached Naisi and Deirdre, who sat playing chess outside their cottage. 'Listen. It is the cry of an Ulsterman,' said Naisi. Deirdre, too, heard, but with growing apprehension, pretended she had not. 'It was only the wind.' Again Fergus called and, once more, Naisi looked up excitedly. 'Surely, you hear that?'

'No,' replied Deirdre. Yet when Fergus called for the third time, Naisi sprang to his feet. 'It is Fergus. I recognize the call now. They have come at last.' Quickly he sent his brothers to bring Fergus and his party to the house. There, the Ulstermen warmly greeted one another.

'Conor pardons you and, no harm shall come to you while you're in our care,' said Fergus.

Deirdre begged her husband not to go back to Ulster. 'In a dream last night' she began, 'three red-breasted birds came to me. They were from Conor's castle of Emain Machda, and in their beaks they held three drops of honey. Yet when they flew away they took with them three drops of blood. Don't you see Naisi, the three drops of honey are messages of peace brought by Fergus, Dubthach and Cormac. The three drops of blood are the deaths of the three sons of Usna.' However, the brothers were so homesick they ignored her warning. After all, Fergus had given his word, and he was an honourable man.

So next day, at dawn, they sailed to Erin. As the sons of Usna stepped ashore at Dun Borrach, Borrach himself greeted them on Conor's orders, and invited Fergus, Dubthach and Cormac to his castle. 'As for the sons of Usna,' Borrach continued, 'Conor commands you hurry to his castle, where he waits to greet you.'

When Fergus heard this, he was angry for he suspected treachery. Yet, he and his two companions had no choice but to respect their vows as knights. So Usna's sons left them and made their way, with Deirdre, to Conor's castle.

Deirdre begged her
husband not to go back
to Ulster. However, the
brothers were so
homesick they ignored
her warning. Next day, at
dawn, they sailed to Erin.

No sooner were they standing on the green before the castle walls, when Conor's soldiers, armed with swords and spears surrounded them. There were at least fifty men against the brothers who quickly formed a ring to shield Deirdre. And so fiercely did they fight, that none of Conor's warriors could break the circle. Yet neither could the brothers escape from the green without endangering Deirdre's life.

An uneven battle raged all day. As darkness fell, the sons of Usna took turns on guard until dawn. Weak from lack of sleep they knew they could not withstand another attack in the open. So they decided to fight their way to cover within the castle. Linking shields, and with Deirdre between them, they scaled the walls of Emain Machda, killing many defenders. Now Conor called for a truce, offering Naisi and his brothers their places among the Red Knights again, if they put down their weapons. The brothers agreed. But no sooner were they unarmed, than Conor treacherously had them seized and tied up. 'Who will put these traitors to death?' he cried. Three times he asked, only to be met by silence.

However, at Conor's court, was one called Rough-Hand Maine, a prince of Norway, whose father had fallen in battle against Naisi. He stepped forward.

Realising there was no escape, Naisi's brother Arddan shouted. 'Let me be the first to die.' For he did not want to see his brothers killed. 'No,' said Aindle. 'I will be the first.'

'Let us die together, my brothers,' said Naisi. Then he requested Maine to take up his own mighty blade. With a single blow, Maine struck all three brothers down.

Though Conor kept Deirdre at Emain Machda for a full year, she never smiled or spoke. Then one day, as Conor drove her in his open carriage, they passed the place where Naisi was buried. Deirdre threw herself out on to the ground, taking her own life. All the men of Ulster stood and wept, as she was buried alongside her beloved Naisi. And on that very spot two yew trees grew, their branches intertwined.

Pwyll Lord of Dyfed

About six hundred years ago, a set of eleven old Welsh stories was recorded in *The Red Book of Hergest*. They were called the Mabinogion, which meant, simply, 'tales'. Many of the stories in the Mabinogion were taken from the myths of the Celts, a people who long ago inhabited Wales and other parts of western Britain. Among them are several tales of King Arthur as well as other stories of heroic deeds and adventures.

'Pwyll, Lord of Dyfed' is the first story in the Mabinogion and tells how Pwyll angered Arawn, the Lord of Annwn, or the Underworld. Pwyll, however, pays his debt to Arawn and the two lords afterwards become close friends.

L ike most powerful noblemen who owned vast areas of land long ago, Pwyll, Lord of Dyfed loved hunting. He owned a fine pack of hunting dogs, a large stable of horses and far away, on the very edge of his territory, a forest region called Glyn Cuch where there were big herds of deer and wild boar.

Pwyll's lands were so far-flung that it took many hours for him to reach Glyn Cuch from Castle Arbrath, where he lived. One evening, Pwyll and a group of followers left the castle just as the sun was setting and headed towards Glyn Cuch. They planned to enjoy some good hunting next day, and afterwards return to Arbrath with all the deer and boar they had caught.

'We shall have a great banquet when we return' Pwyll promised his companions.

What none of them knew as they rode all night towards Glyn Cuch was that Pwyll would not be returning to Castle Arbrath for a whole year. And during that year, he would have a most unusual adventure.

Just as the sun was rising next day, Pwyll and his companions came to the thick forests at Glyn Cuch. Pwyll decided not to waste time. 'Let the hounds loose!' he ordered. 'We are sure to find ourselves a stag or boar before long.'

Pwyll's pack of hunting dogs raced off into the trees, barking and yelping. Pwyll's companions dug their spurs into their horses' sides and rode off after them. Pwyll stopped only to sound his hunting horn, then spurred his own horse to follow the rest.

Pwyll's horse galloped between the trees, but to his surprise, he could see no sign of his friends or his dogs, although he could hear them. Pwyll turned this way and that, trying to locate the familiar barking of his dogs.

At last, he saw them, far away, pelting along over a field beyond the trees. They were obviously chasing something which Pwyll could not see. All at once, as Pwyll watched, a stag ran out of the trees at the other end of the field, followed by a strange pack of dogs. Pwyll gasped in surprise. He had never seen dogs like these. Their coats were brilliant white and their ears were bright red like fire. It hurt Pwyll's eyes to look at them, but he was too fascinated to turn away.

The strange pack of dogs came hurtling after the stag, caught up with it and then, one or two of them jumped up and brought it crashing to the ground.

Meanwhile, Pwyll's own dogs stood yelping at the side of the field, seemingly afraid and unwilling to interfere. Pwyll felt very angry. 'This is my land and that is my stag!' he muttered to himself. 'Who dares to invade my territory and hunt my animals?'

Pwyll rode quickly between the trees and out across the field until he reached the pack of shining white dogs and the fallen stag. He cracked his whip and lashed one or two of them until they all took fright and ran away. At this, Pwyll's own dogs lost their fear and, barking with excitement, they bounded over to their master.

'The stag is yours,' Pwyll told them and at once his dogs turned on the animal and began tearing at it.

Just then, the sound of a horse approaching reached Pwyll's ears. When it

A stag ran out of the trees at the other end of the field, followed by a strange pack of dogs. Their coats were brilliant white and their ears were bright red like fire.

came in sight, Pwyll saw it was a dappled grey and the rider on its back, clad in rich, brown hunting garments, was a total stranger. Pwyll was about to demand who he was, when the strange horseman shouted at him angrily. 'You have done me a great wrong! The stag was my prize, yet you drove my dogs away and gave it to your own hounds. You have offended me and must be punished for it!'

Pwyll was astounded. The man was an intruder and yet he dared to speak like this to a lord on his own lands. However, there was something about the stranger which made Pwyll feel wary of him, and even a little afraid. So, instead of replying angrily, Pwyll said: 'Stranger, if I have insulted you, I am truly sorry, and will do my best to right this wrong. But first, tell me who you are and where you come from?'

When Pwyll heard the stranger's reply, he was glad he had not spoken angrily, for the man was a lord of enormous and terrible power.

'I am Arawn, Lord of Annwn, the Underworld,' he told Pwyll. 'I am mightier than any lord who rules on Earth. Do you wish to be my friend?'

Pwyll, feeling more and more afraid, said that he did.

'Then you must fight the rebel chieftain Hafgan on my behalf,' Arawn went on. 'Hafgan makes war on me constantly. Get rid of him and I will forget that you have insulted me.'

The sound of a horse approaching reached Pwyll's ears. When it came in sight, Pwyll saw it was a dappled grey and the rider on its back, clad in rich brown hunting garments, was a total stranger.

Pwyll was only too anxious to please the mighty Lord of Annwn and readily agreed to fight Hafgan. But he would have to wait a whole year before he could do so.

'Twelve months from this night,' Arawn continued, 'Hafgan and I are to meet and fight to the death. You will go in my place and strike Hafgan once only. One blow and Hafgan will die. But strike him more than once, and he will regain his strength and make war on me again. Do you understand, Lord Pwyll?'

Pwyll said that he did. Then, Arawn told him that until the fight with Hafgan, Pwyll would have to live in his castle and pretend to *be* the Lord of the Underworld.

'Do not worry, Pwyll,' Arawn said. 'You will look like me, and talk and act like me. I will use my magic to see that this is so. Meanwhile, I will take *your* place for a year, live in your castle at Arbrath and rule your lands for you.'

Pwyll agreed to do everything the Lord of Annwn demanded of him. Obediently, he followed Arawn down beneath the Earth into the Underworld of Annwn. After a time, they reached some gates, and beyond the gates, Pwyll saw a magnificent castle.

'That is my home,' Arawn told him. 'Do not be afraid. Everyone there will think that you are me, and will treat you with the honour and respect that is due to me. Farewell, Lord Pwyll. We shall meet again at Glyn Cuch in a year's time.'

Pwyll went through the gates and followed the long path that led to Arawn's castle. When he reached the castle and went inside, he was amazed at how beautiful it was. There were halls and rooms of enormous size, all of them richly furnished and splendidly decorated. Pwyll explored them all and felt excited at the thought that he would be living in this wonderful place for a whole year. He made his way into the great hall of the castle, a huge chamber with walls hundreds of metres high, and began to pull off his hunting boots.

At once, as if by magic, servants and footmen appeared to help him. They bowed low before Pwyll, then took off his boots and his hunting clothes, which were covered in mud and dust. Again, as if by magic, two knights appeared carrying magnificent robes of gold and brocade for Pwyll to wear.

Pwyll was astounded, but also relieved. 'They really think that I am Arawn,' he thought and felt even more thrilled about the year that lay ahead.

Now, the whole castle seemed to be busy with preparations for welcoming back the Lord of the Underworld. The dining hall was made ready for a great feast and servants clad in rich uniforms bustled to and fro carrying dishes piled high with meats and fruits and other rich food. Knights and earls and other fine nobles came to greet Pwyll and at length, a beautiful lady entered the dining hall. She was dressed in a mass of jewels and a robe of gold satin which glittered and sparkled by the light of torches that blazed from the walls.

Pwyll was escorted to his place at the head of the table, where he sat next to the lady who, he presumed was Arawn's wife. The feast which followed was a wonderful event, more wonderful than Pwyll had ever known. The food was served on golden plates and the wine in golden goblets, and all of it tasted marvellous. Minstrels sang songs and tumblers did tricks to entertain the guests. Pwyll talked with the lady and found her not only very beautiful, but also gracious and amusing, a truly wonderful companion.

Next day, Arawn's knights and nobles arrived to accompany Pwyll on a great hunting expedition. When they returned to the castle in the evening, another great feast awaited him, and the lady again sat next to him, delighting him once more with her talk and her company.

Pwyll passed a whole year in this way, enjoying great luxury at the underworld castle. There was sport and entertainment by day and splendid banquets and music every night. Pwyll took care to rule the lands of Annwn well and he was generous and kind to all Arawn's vassals. Whenever they came to Pwyll with a problem or a dispute, he always settled it wisely and everyone went away satisifed that they had been dealt with fairly and justly. Yet not once did anyone suspect that Pwyll was not really Arawn of Annwn. The power of Arawn's magic was complete.

Inevitably, though, the day of the fight with Hafgan arrived. Pwyll said farewell to the lady and set off with a company of knights for the place set aside for the battle.

Hafgan was already there, waiting for him with his own knights and nobles. He looked powerful and strong, and Pwyll knew he must also be proud, for he had dared to claim the lands of the underworld as his own.

'If I can defeat Hafgan,' Pwyll thought, 'then his lands will become the property of Arawn and my debt to Arawn will be doubly paid.'

Pwyll and Hafgan drew their swords and, spurring their horses, rode swiftly towards each other. They clashed with a tremendous noise of steel striking on steel. Quickly, Pwyll brought his sword slicing down, and cut clean through Hafgan's shield and armour. The blow was so great that Hafgan was thrown from his saddle and crashed to the ground. He lay there, so badly injured that he could not get up.

Suddenly, to Pwyll's surprise, Hafgan called out to him: 'You are not Arawn of Annwn! You are a stranger! What right have you to fight me?'

Pwyll had no time to wonder how Hafgan knew he was not Arawn, before the dying chieftain began begging him: 'Whoever you are, finish the task – strike again and kill me!'

But Pwyll remembered Arawn's warning. A second blow would not kill Hafgan, but enable him to fight on. So, Pwyll shook his head and refused to strike Hafgan again. At this, Hafgan gave a deep sigh and called his knights to carry him away. 'I will die soon,' said Hafgan. 'This stranger is now your lord and you must pay homage to him.'

Now that Pwyll had defeated Hafgan, he took possession of all the chieftain's lands and added them to the territory of the Underworld. Then he set off for Glyn Cuch and the meeting with Arawn which had been arranged the year before.

Arawn was pleased to see Pwyll. He had heard how well Pwyll had ruled Annwn in his place and how he had defeated the rebel Hafgan. 'Our first meeting a year ago began with an insult,' Arawn told Pwyll. 'But we are now firm friends for ever.'

Now, Arawn used his magic to give back to Pwyll his own face and form,

Pwyll brought his sword
slicing down, and cut
clean through Hafgan's
shield and armour.
Hafgan was thrown from
his saddle and crashed to
the ground.

and Arawn himself once more took on his real appearance. Then, after bidding each other farewell, Pwyll rode on towards the Castle of Arbrath and Arawn returned to the Underworld.

In both places, their followers welcomed them warmly, not realising that Pwyll and Arawn had each changed back to their true identity. Pwyll decided to find out how Arawn had governed his lands for the past twelve months. He was very pleased with the reply.

'My lord,' said Pwyll's nobles. 'The year has been the happiest year we can remember. You have been wonderfully wise in your dealings. Your justice has been absolutely fair—no man could argue against it. And your kindness and generosity have been boundless.'

'Arawn has cared for my lands and my people better than I could have done myself,' Pwyll thought, feeling very grateful.

Then, he told his nobles what had happened, and how, without knowing it, they had been governed by the Lord of Annwn. Arawn, too, confessed to his own people that Pwyll had been ruling in his place, and also felt grateful to Pwyll for acting so well and so honourably.

The friendship and respect Arawn and Pwyll felt for each other grew stronger and deeper as time went on. They regularly sent each other gifts. Sometimes fine horses, sometimes new dogs which were faster and more alert at hunting than older breeds. Sometimes, the gifts consisted of beautiful hunting hawks. Always, the two lords spoke of each other with the greatest regard. And as a special mark of honour to Arawn, Pwyll put aside his title Lord of Dyfed and instead took a new title, from the name of the Underworld: Chief of Annwn.

Post Scriptum

These stories you have just read are probably amongst the oldest in the world. Minstrels sang and chanted them down the ages, carried them on long journeys and sometimes altered them so much, we cannot always say what they were like originally. But this we know: as soon as humans could think, they grew curious, and began to ask questions about their own creation and the origins and wonders of the world in which they lived. So people invented gods to explain how they themselves were made, and different people invented different gods – but they often played the same roles.

As you know, not all myths were about gods or the natural world; some of the most stirring and heroic grew up around real events and people like Roland, El Cid and Robin Hood. Their exploits grew over the centuries until it was difficult to distinguish fact from fiction, but their stories are still told, no longer by the bards and minstrels of distant ages, but by the storytellers of today – books, cinema and television.

Four centuries before Christ, the Greek philosopher Plato recommended the telling of myths to children, for he believed they contained the best understanding of life, the deepest truth about human behaviour. Over two thousand years later the French writer Anatole France agreed. He wrote that: 'A country that keeps no legends is doomed to die of cold.' And he was probably right.